STATISTICS IN GEOGRAPHY
FOR A-LEVEL STUDENTS

by John G. Wilson B.A.

Schofield & Sims Ltd. Huddersfield

Preface

0 7217 1061 1

0 7217 1062 X Net Edition

First printed 1984

Reprinted 1987

Reprinted 1989

Reprinted 1991

This book covers the practical component which is becoming increasingly important in 'A' level geography. The needs of the student and the demands of the examination have been paramount in its preparation. The techniques, both statistical and cartographical, which are commonly examined at 'A' level are simply, yet fully explained. They are highlighted by clear worked examples which set them firmly in an appropriate geographical context. Each technique is fully evaluated.

Statistical illustration is rich, varied and within the compass of the sixth-form experience. Similar data for other areas or other times may readily be obtained from printed sources or basic fieldwork. It is hoped that this will encourage the student to look beyond the printed page to investigations of his or her own choosing.

In the firm belief that practice certainly leads to competence—and possibly to perfection—numerous exercises have been included in the text. In order that students may test their skill, an appendix provides answers (where appropriate) to the questions which follow each topic. Teachers, for their own testing purposes, may call upon the questions at the end of each section.

I would like to thank my colleague Mike Dockery for much practical assistance cheerfully and willingly given.

Dedication is extended to Linda, Michael, numerous Johns, Ivan, several Fionas, a handful of Patricias, and indeed to the many generations of sixth-form students whom it has been my pleasure to teach and to learn from. Our difficulties were the seeds of this book.

J.G.W.

Printed in England by Martin's of Berwick.

Contents

The district of Teesdale lies in the south-west corner of County Durham. It straddles the valley from which it takes its name, and has as its focus the small but ancient town of Barnard Castle. From west to east the land rolls down from harsh, bleak Pennine moorlands to the softer, more gentle landscapes on the edge of the Durham coalfield. Fig. 1 sketches the mosaic of civil parishes that make up the administrative district. The parishes are identified in Fig. 2 where they have been divided into two groups. Group A is composed of parishes 1 to 17, which include within their boundaries extensive areas of high and difficult land. The parishes in group B are generally favoured by lower altitude and greater opportunity.

As well as naming the parishes, Fig. 2 gives statistical details of area and population. Statistics of agriculture are afforded by Fig. 127, pages 88 and 89. These figures are accurate facts: they are *data*. They enable us to make statements with accuracy and confidence. Lunedale, for example, is the largest parish. It also has the fewest inhabitants per square kilometre. The parishes of Hunderthwaite and Evenwood

Fig. 1 *The Teesdale Parishes*

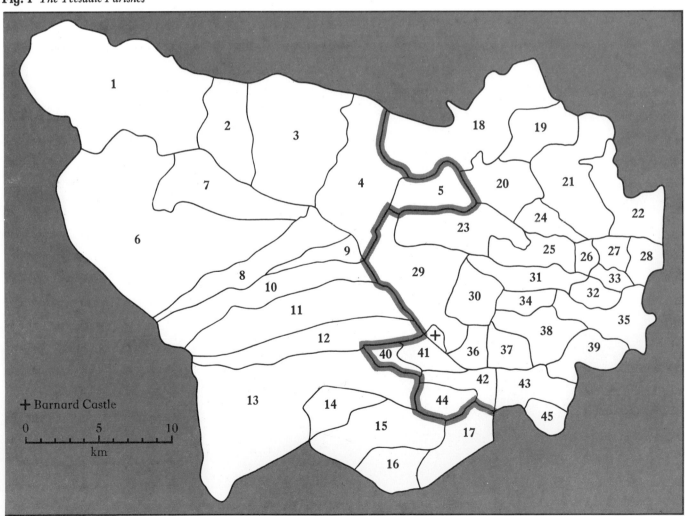

+ Barnard Castle

0   5   10
km

Fig. 2 *Area and population data for the Teesdale Parishes (1981 Census)*

		A	B	C	D
		Area km²	Population (1981)	Population density km² (1981)	% Population change (1971–81)
GROUP A					
1	Forest and Frith	71.6	213	3.0	0
2	Newbiggin	18.8	166	8.8	−1.2
3	Middleton-in-Teesdale	42.5	1196	28.1	−15.3
4	Eggleston	32.5	361	11.1	+9.7
5	Woodland	11.7	223	19.1	+0.9
6	Lunedale	92.2	105	1.1	−2.8
7	Holwick	23.5	77	3.3	+4.1
8	Mickleton	19.3	368	19.1	+5.8
9	Romaldkirk	5.5	188	34.2	+14.6
10	Hunderthwaite	25.5	124	4.9	+4.2
11	Cotherstone	33.2	509	15.3	+3.2
12	Lartington	21.9	133	6.1	+11.8
13	Bowes	68.7	448	6.5	+9.5
14	Gilmonby	10.0	52	5.2	+13.0
15	Scargill	21.0	37	1.8	−19.6
16	Hope	10.5	18	1.7	0
17	Barningham	14.3	191	13.4	+8.5
GROUP B		A	B	C	D
18	South Bedburn	40.8	190	4.7	+8.6
19	Hamsterley	12.1	387	32.0	+20.6
20	Lynesack & Softley	15.1	1238	82.0	−8.6
21	Evenwood & Barony	25.0	2996	119.8	+0.4
22	Etherley	16.6	1658	99.9	−6.4
23	Langleydale & Shotton	18.9	75	4.0	+7.1
24	Cockfield	6.5	1792	275.7	−3.4
25	Raby with Keverstone	11.4	103	9.0	−3.7
26	Wackerfield	3.0	52	17.3	−14.8
27	Hilton	4.4	60	13.6	+1.7
28	*Bolam/Morton Tinmouth	5.8	93	16.0	−7.0
29	Marwood	29.3	401	13.7	+42.2
30	Streatlam & Stainton	11.9	608	51.1	−24.6
31	Staindrop	8.1	1223	151.0	+10.8
32	Langton	4.4	47	10.7	+6.8
33	Ingleton	3.4	309	90.9	−4.3
34	Cleatlam	4.7	67	14.3	−17.3
35	*Gainford/Headlam	12.8	1361	106.3	−0.9
36	Westwick	5.9	77	13.1	−18.9
37	Whorlton	8.0	165	20.6	0
38	Winston	12.3	465	37.8	+12.6
39	*Barforth/Ovington	9.2	208	22.6	−3.3
40	Boldron	5.0	84	16.8	−4.5
41	*Startforth/Egglestone Abbey	6.7	1034	154.3	+72.3
42	Rokeby	4.7	89	18.9	−6.3
43	Wycliffe with Thorpe	10.2	79	7.7	−35.8
44	Brignall	8.6	90	10.5	+13.9
45	Hutton Magna	5.3	76	14.3	−20.8

& Barony differ little in area but much in population. Twenty-two parishes recorded an increase in population between 1971 and 1981. Such statements, accurate though they may be, are of limited value to the geographer who is more interested in what the *sets* of data may reveal. How, for instance, do the two groups of parishes compare in terms of area or land use? Is the contrast in relief reflected in parish size? Have people responded to the greater opportunities afforded by the lower land? A glance at the data may suggest an answer, but mere perusal of figures seldom produces a sure answer, and fails to indicate the extent of any relationship. Data such as that presented in Fig. 2 is too lengthy and too complex for us to make direct deductions. It needs to be reduced to simple figures that accurately describe or summarise the data and, by facilitating comparisons, highlight the spatial variations which lie at the heart of geography.

The first step on the road to simplification is to find average values. 'Average', however, is a word to be treated with caution. It means one thing in general conversation, but the statistician recognises several 'averages'. It is therefore safer to speak of *measures of central tendency*.

Measures of Central Tendency

Arithmetic Mean

Arithmetic mean, usually abbreviated to 'mean', is the 'average' in common use. It is found by totalling the values in a data set and dividing by the number of items. Expressed as a formula it is:

$$\bar{x} = \frac{\Sigma x}{n}$$

where $\bar{x}$ (x-bar) = mean
Σ (Sigma) = the sum of
x = the values of the variable
n = the number of items in the set

Consider an example from the Teesdale parishes, group A. To find mean parish area (the variable), the values of individual parishes (x) are added to give a total (Σx) of 522.7 km². This, divided by 17 (n) gives a result of 30.75 km², which, to the customary two decimal places, is the required mean.

For parishes in group B, with $\Sigma x = 310.1$ km² and $n = 28$ the mean is 11.08 km². Comparison of the two mean values gives a precise picture of the contrast in area between upland and lowland parishes.

* Because of the limitations of scale, two small parishes have been combined.

1 Consider the data given in Fig. 2. For each group of parishes, calculate:
  a mean total population;
  b mean population density;
  c mean percentage population change.

Often, the required data is available only in the form of groups or classes. A typical situation is illustrated by Fig. 3. *Grouped data* such as this cannot yield a precise mean, but an acceptable approximation may be calculated. To find the mean size of landholding in the parish of Boldron, for example, the data is first tabled as in Fig. 4. Simple calculation gives the mid-class value, and this is multiplied by the number of landholdings in each class to give the figure recorded in the last column. This column is then summed and divided by the total number of landholdings in Boldron to give the required mean.

In mathematical language:

$$\bar{x} = \frac{\Sigma(fx_0)}{\Sigma f}$$

where $\bar{x}$ = mean
  Σ = sum of
  f = number of occurrences (frequency)
  x_0 = mid-class value

In the above example, $\bar{x} = \dfrac{482.5}{13} = 37.12$ ha.

It is stressed that this method only gives an approximate value. It is most reliable when classes are small and frequency high.

2 From data given in Fig. 3, calculate the mean size of landholding in the parishes of:
  a Barningham;
  b Wycliffe with Thorpe;
  c Bolam/Morton Tinmouth;
  d Hilton.

Fig. 3 *Grouped data : often the required data is available only in the form of groups or classes*

Area under crops and grass (hectares)	Number of landholdings				
	Boldron	Barningham	Wycliffe with Thorpe	Bolam/ Morton Tinmouth	Hilton
5 and under 10	1	0	1	0	0
10 and under 20	3	2	1	2	2
20 and under 30	5	1	1	1	1
30 and under 40	1	1	1	0	1
40 and under 50	1	2	1	0	0
50 and under 100	1	1	1	2	3
100 and under 200	1	2	3	1	0

Fig. 4 *Table to find the mean size of landholdings in Boldron*

Class (hectares)	Mid-class value (x_0)	No. of occurrences (f)	(fx_0)
5 and under 10	7.5	1	7.5
10 and under 20	15.0	3	45.0
20 and under 30	25.0	5	125.0
30 and under 40	35.0	1	35.0
40 and under 50	45.0	1	45.0
50 and under 100	75.0	1	75.0
100 and under 200	150.0	1	150.0
		$\Sigma f = 13$	$\Sigma(fx_0) = 482.5$

Median

The *median* is simply the mid-point in a set of values. Let the parish areas in group A serve as an example. The values must first be ranked in descending order. It is tempting, but rash, to rank by observation. Time and temper will be saved, and the risk of error reduced, if values are taken in sequence and positioned in order of size against a line drawn on a piece of scrap paper. Fig. 5a provides illustration. With 17 values in the set, the ninth will be the median for there are eight above and eight below. Fig. 5a arrows the median of 21.9 km².

To find the median of the areas of group B is less straightforward. This group has 28 parishes—an even number. There is no central value. When a data set has an even number of items, the median is found by taking the mean of the two middle values. In Fig. 5b the two middle values are 8.6 and 8.1, the mean of which is 8.35 km². This, then, is the median. There are fourteen values above and fourteen below. It is important to note that 8.35 is not one of the values in the data set.

3 Consider the data given in Fig. 2. For each group of parishes, find the median value of:
  a population;
  b population density;
  c percentage population change.

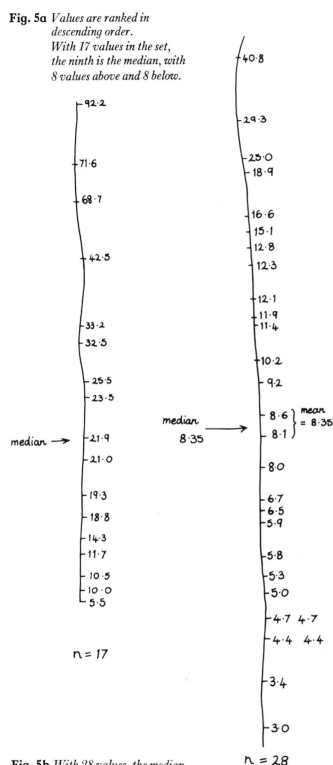

Fig. 5a *Values are ranked in descending order. With 17 values in the set, the ninth is the median, with 8 values above and 8 below.*

median →

n = 17

Fig. 5b *With 28 values, the median is the mean of the two middle values. There are 14 values above and 14 below*

n = 28

Mode

The *mode* is defined as the value which occurs most frequently in a series. A simple example will illustrate. The figures printed in Fig. 6 represent the number of residents in each of twenty houses in a suburban avenue. With such an uncomplicated set of data, it is tempting to find the mode by observation, but to avoid risk of error, which can be considerable with more complex data, the method given in Fig. 7 is suggested. Each figure is considered in turn and ticked off against the appropriate household size. When the ticks are totalled, 4 has the highest score. The mode of household size in this particular avenue is therefore 4.

Fig. 6 *The figures represent the number of residents in each of 20 houses*

| 5 | 4 | 2 | 2 | 4 | 4 | 6 | 1 | 3 | 4 |
| 3 | 5 | 3 | 3 | 4 | 4 | 5 | 2 | 3 | 4 |

Fig. 7 *Table to find the mode of a set of values. The mode of household size is 4*

Household size	Tally	Total or frequency (f)
1	✓	1
2	✓ ✓ ✓	3
3	✓ ✓ ✓ ✓ ✓	5
4	✓ ✓ ✓ ✓ ✓ ✓ ✓	7
5	✓ ✓ ✓	3
6	✓	1

The data in this example is described as *discrete*. It was obtained by counting, and is presented in neat whole numbers. Sadly, most data is *continuous*. It is obtained by measurement or calculation, processes which lead to an almost infinite range of decimal values. In Fig. 2, page 5, population is the sole example of discrete data. Clear modes are rare with continuous data, or even with discrete data when the range of values is large. Further examination of Fig. 2 will provide illustration of this point.

If a precise mode is not evident, we can at least come close by finding the *modal class*. For this, the data is grouped into an appropriate number of classes, and the one which holds the greatest number of values is the one we seek.

In the search for modal class, the first and most difficult step is to decide on the number and size of the classes into which the data is to be grouped. With too few groups, detail is lost: with too many the data is spread too thinly. A fixed class interval is generally necessary.

There are no hard and fast rules to help us in the search. Often it is a question of trial and error illuminated by wise judgement based on experience. The following example

7

illustrates a popular approach. It is based on data of area of Teesdale parishes group A (Fig. 2).

A guide to the maximum number of classes is provided by the mathematical expression $5 \times \log n$. In this example, with 17 parishes, this equals $5 \times \log 17 = 5 \times 1.23 = 6.15$. Thus, 6 classes can be adopted as the maximum.

Next, examine the *range* of the data. The smallest parish area is 5·5 km², the largest is 92.2 km², and the range is therefore 86.7 km². Now seek a close and convenient round number, preferably one with a choice of factors. In this case, 90 is appropriate. Division of 90 by 6 (the suggested maximum number of classes) gives a class interval of 15.

Fig. 8 *5–19.9̇ is the modal class—it claims more values than any other*

Class	Tally	Frequency
5–19.9̇	✓✓✓✓✓✓ ✓✓✓✓✓✓	7
20–34.9̇	✓✓✓✓✓✓	6
35–49.9̇	✓	1
50–64.9̇		0
65–79.9̇	✓✓	2
80–94.9̇	✓	1

Classes are detailed to the left of Fig. 8. Note how they are identified. The first class accommodates all values from 5 km² up to, but not including, 20 km². 19.9 recurring (19.9̇) is a convenient way of setting the upper limit. If this were not done, it would be difficult to place values such as 20 km² and 35 km². Values are tallied against classes and totalled In Fig. 8 it is seen that the first class, 5 – 19.9̇, claims more values than any other. 5 – 19.9̇ is the modal class.

One or two further points are worthy of note. In deciding on the number of classes, we are not restricted to the maximum indicated by $5 \times \log n$. In the above example, for instance, 5 classes with an interval of 18 would be acceptable. The expression of modal class will, of course, vary slightly with the choice of class interval. In fixing the class interval, whole numbers are convenient and desirable, but not essential. Decimals often afford the most suitable division. The range of data in the above example can, in fact, be adequately covered by 6 classes with an interval of 14·5.

Look again at Fig. 8. It will be noted that no values fall within the class 50 – 64·9̇. This is not ideal. Empty classes are best avoided, perhaps by reducing the number of classes. This is not always easy, especially when, as here, n is small and the range is considerable.

Finally, a set of data may have two modes or two modal classes. Such a set is described as *bimodal*.

4 Consider the data given in Fig. 15 (page 12). Find the modal class of annual rainfall at:
  a Station A;
  b Station B.

5 For Teesdale parishes group B (Fig. 2), give the modal class of:
  a area;
  b population;
  c percentage population change.

Of the measures of central tendency, the mean is the one most commonly quoted. It takes all values into consideration. It is easy to calculate, yet precise, and its significance is readily appreciated. It may, however, be unduly influenced by one or two extreme values, and, with discrete data, it can yield a figure that is less than appropriate. The mean of the household size data in Fig. 6 is 3.55 persons. This is a perfectly accurate measure, but one that is difficult to relate to reality. The modal class lacks the precision that is a feature of the mean, but the sacrifice is well worth while if a 'typical' figure is required. A mode of 4 may be considered more relevant to household size than a mean of 3.55. The median is the half-way house in ranked data. It is not influenced by extreme values, and is most useful when the majority of values in a data set are clustered near the highest or lowest. It is rare for mean, median and mode to coincide for each is the result of a different interpretation of the central tendency. Which is most useful will depend largely on the nature of the data, but as each makes a distinctive contribution to the description of data, it is often wise to quote all three.

The measures of central tendency are valuable and precise summaries and facilitate vital comparisons between data sets. They do not, however, tell the whole story. Look, for instance, at the two sets of data in Fig. 9. In each case the swiftest glance reveals a median of 50, and the same figure is also the mean of both. Yet, as Fig. 10 emphasises, these simple data sets are not identical. There is a profound difference in the way that the values are dispersed about the measures of central tendency.

Thus, a full description of a data set needs an additional dimension. This is provided by the *measures of dispersion*.

Fig. 9 *The median of each set is 50 and the same figure is also the mean but the data sets are not identical*

A	80	70	60	50	40	30	20
B	53	52	51	50	49	48	47

Fig. 10 *The dispersion of the values of sets A and B (Fig. 9)*

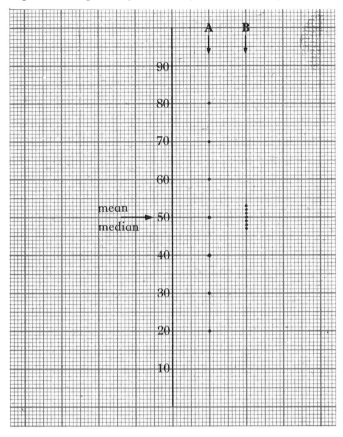

Interquartile Range

This is a most useful measure of how values are dispersed about the median. The first step in the quest for the interquartile range is to rank the data and find the median as described on page 6. For the population density of parishes group A, this has been done in Fig. 11. The median is 6.5. The *upper quartile* is the median of the values above 6.5. Here, with eight values, it is the mean of 19.1 and 15.3, that is, 17.2. Similarly, the lower quartile is 3.15, the mean of 3.3 and 3.0. Subtraction of *lower quartile* from upper quartile gives an interquartile range of 14.05.

It is to be noted that if the interquartile range is divided by 2, another measure of dispersion is produced. This is known as the *quartile deviation*.

A small interquartile range (or quartile deviation) indicates that values are closely clustered about the median. Higher figures indicate wider dispersion. Simple illustration of this can be obtained from Fig. 9. The interquartile range of the scattered values in set A is 40, whereas the figure for set B is only 4.

Fig. 11 *The interquartile range for the population density of group A parishes*

$$
\text{mean} = 17.2 \begin{cases} 34.2 \\ 28.1 \\ 19.1 \quad 19.1 \\ 15.3 \end{cases} \text{upper quartile} \quad 17.2
$$

$$
\begin{matrix} 13.4 \\ 11.1 \\ 8.8 \\ 6.5 \longleftarrow \text{median} \\ 6.1 \\ 5.2 \\ 4.9 \end{matrix}
$$

$$
\text{mean} = 3.15 \begin{cases} 3.3 \\ 3.0 \end{cases} \text{lower quartile} \quad 3.15
$$

$$
\begin{matrix} 1.8 \\ 1.7 \\ 1.1 \end{matrix}
$$

interquartile range = 14.05

Measures of Dispersion

Range

To obtain this measure (already encountered in discussion of modal class) the lowest value in a data set is subtracted from the highest. In group A parishes (Fig. 2), the largest has an area of 92.2 km², whereas the smallest is only 5.5 km². The range is 86.7 km². For group B parishes, the range is 37.8 km² (40.8–3.0). A contrast between the two groups is clearly evident.

Range is the simplest of the measures of dispersion, but it is generally the least informative. It emphasises the extremes and says little about the distribution of the remainder.

6 Determine the interquartile range of each set of data in Fig. 5, page 7.

7 For each group of parishes (Fig. 2), determine the interquartile range of:
a population;
b percentage population change.

Mean Deviation

This, as its name suggests, is a measure of the dispersion of a set of values about the mean. It is obtained with the help of the simple formula:

$$\frac{\Sigma |x - \bar{x}|}{n}$$

where Σ = sum of
n = the number of values in the set.

The expression $|x - \bar{x}|$ tells us that the mean is to be subtracted from each value in turn, and that the sign (plus or minus) is to be ignored. Fig. 12 provides a worked example. The higher the mean deviation, the greater the degree of dispersion.

---

 8 For each group of parishes (Fig. 2), calculate the mean deviation of:
  a population;
  b population density.

Standard Deviation

This is the most commonly used measure of the dispersion about the mean. It is not obtained quickly, but a pocket calculator will eliminate much tedious arithmetic, especially if equipped with keys for x^2 and $\sqrt{}$. The now familiar areas of parishes group A again serve as example. A four-column table is prepared, with headings as indicated in Fig. 13. The values of the variable (x), in this case area in km², are inserted accurately in the second column. The mean is calculated and recorded in a prominent position at the head of the table. For column three, the mean is subtracted in turn from the area of each parish ($x - \bar{x}$). This gives both plus and minus values, but the latter disappear when the figure is squared as required for the fourth column. The figures in the fourth column are totalled to give $\Sigma(x - \bar{x})^2$, which in our example is 9671·22. Now, substitution can be made in the formula for standard deviation which is:

$$\sigma = \sqrt{\frac{\Sigma(x - \bar{x})^2}{n}}$$

where σ (sigma) is the symbol for standard deviation
n = the number of items in the set (in this case 17).

Fig. 12 *Finding the mean deviation*

Parish area—group A   Mean area ($\bar{x}$) = 30·75 km²

Parish	Area (km²) x	$|x - \bar{x}|$
1	71.6	40.85
2	18.8	11.95
3	42.5	11.75
4	32.5	1.75
5	11.7	19.05
6	92.2	61.45
7	23.5	7.25
8	19.3	11.45
9	5.5	25.25
10	25.5	5.25
11	33.2	2.45
12	21.9	8.85
13	68.7	37.95
14	10.0	20.75
15	21.0	9.75
16	10.5	20.25
17	14.3	16.45

$\Sigma|x - \bar{x}| = 312\cdot45$

Mean deviation $= \dfrac{\Sigma|x-\bar{x}|}{n} = \dfrac{312\cdot45}{17} = 18\cdot38$

Fig. 13 *Preparatory table for calculating standard deviation*

Parish area—group A   Mean area ($\bar{x}$) = 30·75 km²

Parish	Area (km²) x	$x - \bar{x}$	$(x - \bar{x})^2$
1	71.6	40.85	1668.72
2	18.8	−11.95	142.80
3	42.5	11.75	138.06
4	32.5	1.75	3.06
5	11.7	−19.05	362.90
6	92.2	61.45	3776.10
7	23.5	−7.25	52.56
8	19.3	−11.45	131.10
9	5.5	−25.25	637.56
10	25.5	−5.25	27.56
11	33.2	2.45	6.00
12	21.9	−8.85	78.32
13	68.7	37.95	1440.20
14	10.0	−20.75	430.56
15	21.0	−9.75	95.06
16	10.5	−20.25	410.06
17	14.3	−16.45	270.60

$\Sigma(x - \bar{x})^2 = 9671.22$

Thus,

$$\sigma = \sqrt{\frac{9671.22}{17}}$$

$$\sigma = \sqrt{568.90}$$

$$\therefore \sigma = 23.85 \text{ km}^2$$

The figure of 23.85 is a rather high value for standard deviation, and it indicates that the values are widely spread about the mean. A lower value would indicate a closer grouping.

An alternative method is provided by the formula:

$$\sigma = \sqrt{\frac{\Sigma x^2}{n} - \bar{x}^2}.$$

This eliminates the need for numerous subtractions, but if the values of the variable are large, it may demand the manipulation of somewhat ungainly figures.

A number of calculations such as those involved in Fig. 13 often prove daunting to the student. Understandably so. On reflection, however, it will be appreciated that there is nothing difficult in any of the operations involved. Patience and care are the required qualities. Most errors arise from undue haste. Take these simple precautions. Write the figures clearly and distinctly. Arrange them neatly, with decimal points exactly beneath one another. Take the trouble to check your calculations at each stage.

 For each group of parishes (Fig. 2), calculate the standard deviation of:
a population;
b population density;
c percentage population change.

Standard deviation is the most powerful of the measures of dispersion. It must be noted, however, that it is tightly bound to the mean of a particular data set. The degree of dispersion that it represents will vary with the mean. If two data sets have the same standard deviation but different means, dispersion will be greater where the mean is lower. Hence, when two or more data sets are to be compared in respect of dispersion, a further measure is prescribed. A choice is available in the *measures of variability*.

Measures of Variability

There are three of these, each derived from a simple formula:

$$\text{Coefficient of variation } (v) = \frac{\text{standard deviation}}{\text{mean}} \times 100$$

$$\text{Index of variability} = \frac{\text{quartile deviation}}{\text{median}} \times 100$$

$$\text{Relative variability} = \frac{\text{mean deviation}}{\text{mean}} \times 100$$

Of the three, the coefficient is the most frequently encountered. Note that all three are expressed as percentages. The higher the percentage, the greater the variability of the data under examination.

 For each group of parishes (Fig. 2), calculate the coefficient of variation of:
a area;
b population;
c population density.

The measures of central tendency, dispersion, and variability are the products of precise mathematical techniques, but technique must not be regarded as an end in itself. Its role in the description and analysis of geographical problems must be appreciated. The geographer must look through the data at the reality it represents. Two examples will illustrate this very important point.

Suppose that the crest line of a cuesta is examined on a topographical map, and heights above sea-level are recorded at, say, 1-kilometre intervals. This data may readily be processed to give mathematically precise figures for mean and standard deviation. To the geographer, mere figures are of little interest in themselves. They demand interpretation. "What do they mean?" is the question asked. A mean of, say, 200 metres is appreciated as an indication of the general height of the cuesta. Standard deviation will add further detail. If its value is low, departures from mean height are likely to be few and modest, and a crest of roughly uniform height is described. If standard deviation is large, the crest will be more irregular, with significant peaks and valleys.

Fig. 14 is an attempt to express this idea in visual terms. Each rectangle represents the view of a different cuesta as seen through the lens of a distant camera. Mean altitude is

Fig. 14 *Mean altitude is the same in each case, but the greater the degree of dissection the higher the value for standard deviation*

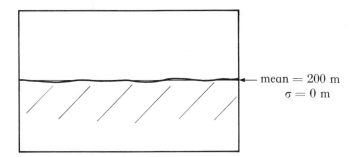

mean = 200 m
σ = 0 m

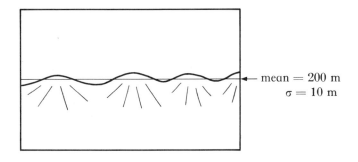

mean = 200 m
σ = 10 m

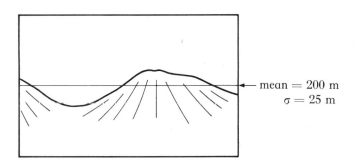

mean = 200 m
σ = 25 m

the same in each case but the higher the value for standard deviation, the greater the degree of dissection. In describing or comparing land-forms, words may be inadequate or imprecise. With mean and standard deviation to hand, description of relief can be quantified.

Consider a further example. The data in Fig. 15 represents annual rainfall totals at two widely separated stations over a period of twenty-five years. There is little difference in the mean, so both stations are roughly similar in the amount of precipitation they receive. But note the higher value of standard deviation at B. This is of more than passing mathematical interest, for it has important practical significance. It reveals that annual rainfall at B is subject to greater fluctuation. To the farmer, B is a more hazardous environment, where he would expect occasional years of drought or excessive rainfall when yields would be poor and income low. The data in Fig. 15 would also have practical significance for the water engineer, to whom flood control and the provision of storage facilities are important.

---

11 A student investigated the altitude, in metres, achieved by the sides of a moorland valley and expressed his findings as follows:

	West	East
$\bar{x}$	190	240
σ	13	27

How would you interpret his findings?

12 Analysis of the yield in tonnes per hectare of a particular crop in two areas over a period of fifteen years produced the following:

	Area A	Area B
$\bar{x}$	7.3	10.1
σ	6.1	4.9

Comment on these figures.

Fig. 15 *Annual rainfall totals at two widely separated stations over a period of 25 years*

Station A
71 93 63 74 71 82 65 79 55 86
84 70 79 98 75 89 71 79 68 75
81 83 61 74 74

$\bar{x}$ = 76.4 cm σ = 9.9 cm

Station B
59 90 86 36 53 123 90 43 111 68
74 79 99 58 73 38 120 60 68 77
89 80 78 87 48

$\bar{x}$ = 75.5 cm σ = 22.9 cm

Visual Representation of Data

The dispersion of values in a data set may often be more easily appreciated if presented in a visual form, and for this a variety of techniques are available. Perhaps the simplest is the *dispersion diagram*.

Dispersion Diagrams

Fig. 10 (page 9) is a simple example already encountered. A vertical scale covering the range of the data is drawn, and values are dotted alongside at appropriate points. Fig. 16 is a more elaborate example based on the rainfall data given in Fig. 15. The greater variability of annual rainfall at B is clearly evident. The values of median and quartiles may be arrowed to facilitate comparisons. Dispersion diagrams are also useful in identifying significant breaks in a sequence of data.

13 Draw dispersion diagrams for the area of Teesdale parishes groups A and B. Take the data from Fig. 2 (page 5) but round off to the nearest whole number. Indicate by arrows the median and quartile values.

14 For each group of parishes (Fig. 2), draw dispersion diagrams to illustrate:
a population;
b population density;
c percentage population change.

Graphs of Frequency Distribution

By recording every value, the dispersion diagram paints a precise picture of a distribution. Less detailed, but generally more useful are the *graphs of frequency distribution*.

Histogram

This is an effective and popular way of depicting the distribution of values in a data set. Its use is confined to grouped data, and grouping into classes as described on page 7 is usually an essential preliminary. This has been done in Fig. 17 for the rainfall data for station A (Fig. 15). Six classes with an interval of 7.5 were judged the most suitable. Class limits are given in column A, and frequency is recorded alongside in column B. (The remaining columns may be ignored for the moment.) Fig. 18 is the histogram drawn from this data. The scale on the vertical (or y) axis accommodates frequency. The horizontal (or x) axis is marked off into classes. The labelling of these classes is sometimes a source of confusion. By convention, numbers indicate the starting-point of the class to the right. Thus, a value of 69 cm falls into the third class from the left, and

Fig. 16 *Dispersion diagrams of the rainfall data for stations A and B (Fig. 15)*

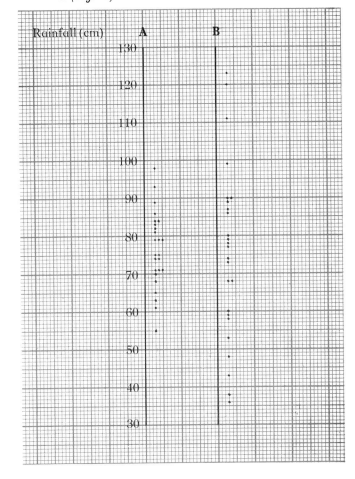

Fig. 17 *Grouped data for the rainfall at Station A (Fig. 15)*

A	B	C	D	E
Class limits	f	$\%f$	Cumulative f	Cumulative % frequency
54 – 61.4	2	8	2	8
61.5 – 68.9	3	12	5	20
69 – 76.4	8	32	13	52
76.5 – 83.9	6	24	19	76
84 – 91.4	4	16	23	92
91.5 – 98.9	2	8	25	100

$n = 25$

Fig. 18 *Histogram of rainfall data at Station A*

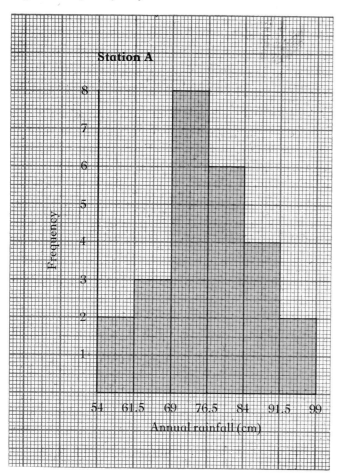

15 Draw a histogram of the rainfall data for station B in Fig. 15, page 12.

16 Taking appropriate data for each group of parishes from Fig. 127 (pages 88 and 89), draw histograms of:
a mean farm size;
b percentage of farmland rented.

Histograms may also be drawn to show percentage frequency. Look again at Fig. 17. Column C records the results of simple percentage calculations. The lowest class, for example, claims 2 out of a total of 25 occurrences, and $2/25 \times 100$ gives a percentage of 8. The histogram based on the figures in column C is seen in Fig. 19. Apart from the division of the vertical scale, construction is exactly as described for Fig. 18.

Fig. 19 *Percentage frequency histogram of rainfall data at Station A*

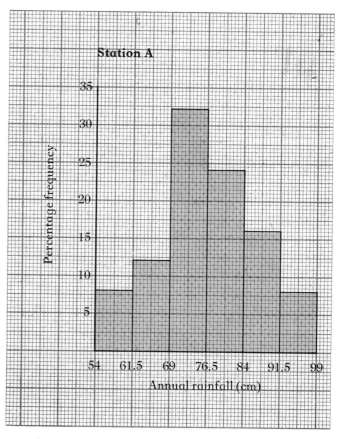

84 cm into the fifth. Further examination of Fig. 18 reveals how frequency, the number of values in a class, is indicated by bars of appropriate height. Study of histograms can be most instructive, for they store useful data, and give a good visual impression of distribution.

The histogram, although basically a simple graph, demands care and judgement in its production. Needless to say, it must be accurately drawn, but also it should like all graphs, be well presented. Bars should not be too thick or too thin, and the vertical scale should not shoot skywards. The overall size of the histogram should be modest; do not aim to fill a page when a quarter would be more appropriate. Graph paper is useful. It helps in the division of scales, and provides ready-made parallel lines, but legibility usually demands that the bars be lightly shaded. The axes should be labelled, the units quoted and the whole rounded off with a title.

17 Draw a percentage frequency histogram of the rainfall data for station B (Fig. 15, page 12).

18 For each group of Teesdale parishes, draw a percentage frequency histogram for:
  a population density;
  b percentage population change.
  See Fig. 2, page 5, for data.

Histograms are most useful in the visual comparison of two or more data sets. A common class interval is an essential requirement, and the horizontal axis must span the full range of data of both sets. If the data sets are not of equal size, percentage frequency histograms are preferred. Fig. 20 provides illustration, and the contrasts between the two groups of parishes are immediately apparent.

19 For each group of Teesdale parishes, draw a percentage frequency histogram of the data contained in Fig. 127 (pages 88 and 89), for:
  a mean farm size;
  b percentage of farmland rented.
  Comment briefly on any contrasts between the data sets as highlighted by the histograms.

It must be stressed that the histogram is only used to graph the frequency distribution of grouped data. When data is not grouped, a simple line chart is appropriate. Household size (Fig. 7, page 7) is used for the example shown in Fig. 21.

Fig. 20 *Percentage frequency histograms to show percentage of farmland in improved grass in parishes in groups A and B*

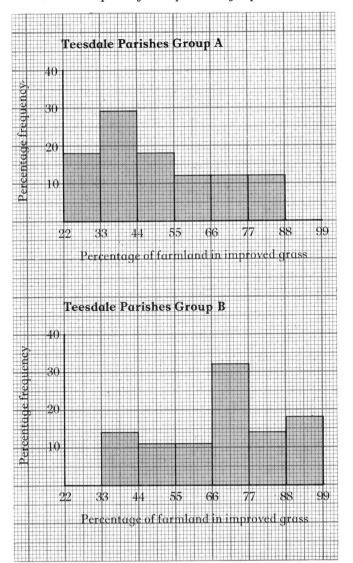

Fig. 21 *Line chart of household size data*

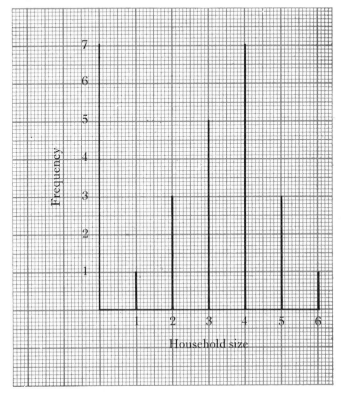

Frequency Polygon

A frequency polygon of the rainfall data for station A (Fig. 15) is drawn in Fig. 22. Comparison with Fig. 18 will reveal that it has much in common with the histogram. Both employ the same axes and scales to graph the distribution of values in a data set. The difference lies in the way frequency is plotted. With the polygon, the number of occurrences is dotted where a vertical line through the mid-point of the class reaches the appropriate height on the vertical scale. The points are joined by a series of straight lines, and the graph is extended to the horizontal axis at half the class interval beyond the limits of the scale. Empty classes are similarly accommodated.

Percentage frequency polygons provide an alternative to percentage histograms for the comparison of the distribution of values in data sets of unequal size. When horizontal scales are compatible, one pair of axes may carry two or more polygons which, suitably distinguished in line or colour, enable immediate visual comparison.

If the points plotted for Fig. 22 had been joined, not by straight lines, but by a smooth curve, a *frequency curve* rather than a polygon would have been the result. Unless the class interval is very very small, frequency curves tend to be inaccurate, and for this reason, polygons are usually preferred. Diagrammatic frequency curves are, however, often used to give a quick visual impression of a distribution.

---

20 For the rainfall data for station B (Fig. 15, page 12) draw:
   a a frequency polygon;
   b a percentage frequency polygon;
   c a frequency curve.

21 Using data from Fig. 127 (pages 88 and 89), for each group of parishes draw a percentage frequency polygon of:
   a percentage of farmland rented;
   b mean farm size.
   In each case comment comparatively on the distribution of values displayed.

22 Using data from Fig. 127, for each group of parishes, draw percentage frequency polygons for the percentage of farmland in improved grass. Compare them with the histograms presented in Fig. 20 (page 15). Which technique do you consider most effectively illustrates the contrast in the distribution of values?

Fig. 22 *Frequency polygon of rainfall data at Station A*

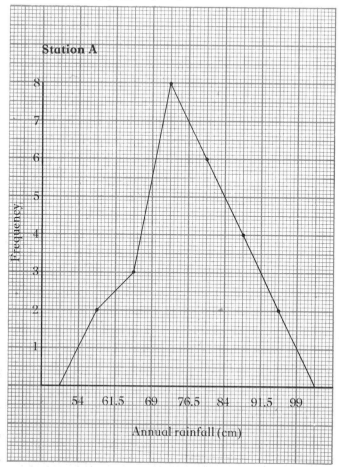

Cumulative Frequency Curve

Turn once more to Fig. 17. Column D contains figures for cumulative frequency, and comparison with column B will reveal how they were achieved. Data in the cumulative form may be presented as a cumulative frequency curve or *ogive*. Fig. 23 illustrates construction. The now familiar class intervals are shown on the horizontal axis, and the vertical axis carries the scale of cumulative frequency. Values are plotted against the right-hand side of the class division.

Fig. 24 is the percentage version based on the figures in column E of Fig. 17. Its use in identifying median and quartiles is illustrated, but it must be noted that, because data is grouped, answers can only be approximate.

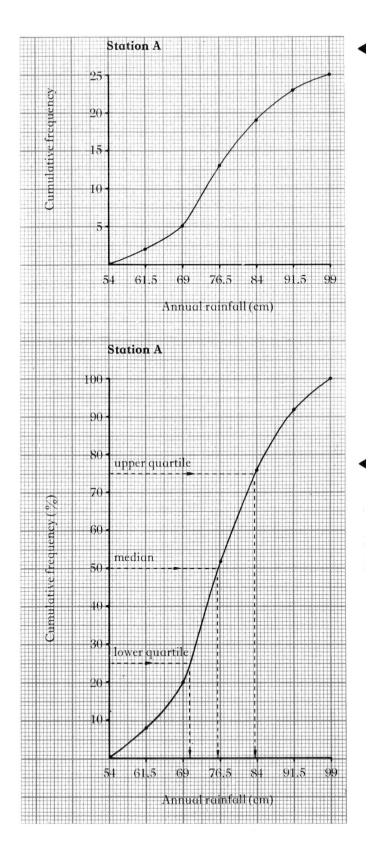

◀ **Fig. 23** *Cumulative frequency curve to show distribution of rainfall at Station A*

---

23 For the rainfall data for station B (Fig. 15, page 12), draw:
a a cumulative frequency curve;
b a cumulative percentage frequency curve.

Use data from Fig. 2, page 5, and Fig. 127, pages 88 and 89, to answer the following questions.

24 For Teesdale parishes group A, draw cumulative frequency curves of the data for:
a population density;
b area.

25 For Teesdale parishes group B, draw cumulative frequency curves of the data for:
a population density;
b area.

26 For each group of parishes, draw a cumulative percentage frequency curve to illustrate the percentage of farmland in improved grass. Compare the curves with the histograms seen in Fig. 20 (page 15). Which technique do you consider most effectively illustrates the contrast in the distribution of values?

◀ **Fig. 24** *Percentage cumulative frequency curve to show distribution of rainfall at Station A, together with median and quartile values*

The Shape of Frequency Distributions

The histogram, in the height of its columns, gives shape to a distribution. So, too, in their own particular way, do frequency polygons and ogives. Shape varies with data and the range of possibilities is immense. Two general shapes that are commonly encountered are illustrated diagrammatically in Fig. 25, where frequency curves are superimposed on histograms. In (a), frequency is greatest among the lower values of the variable, and tails off to the right. The reverse is shown in (b). These asymmetrical distributions are described as *skewed*. Fig. 25(a) is an example of positive skew, whereas Fig. 25(b) shows negative skew. It is worth noting the effect of skew on the relationship of the measures of central tendency. Mean, median and mode are indicated diagrammatically in Fig. 25. The mode, by its nature, corresponds to the summit of the curve. Median and mean, in that order, slip down the slope to the 'tail'. If these positions are translated into values (identified on the horizontal scale), positive skew displays a mean that is greater

17

Fig. 25 *Skewed distributions*

a Positive skew

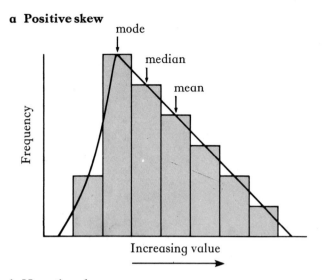

b Negative skew

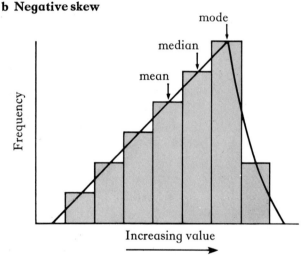

Fig. 26 *A normal curve of distribution*

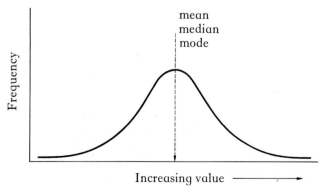

than the median, which in its turn is greater than the mode. With negative skew, the reverse is true. The degree of skewness varies with different distributions. As it increases, so, too, does the disparity between the measures of central tendency. Hence, in highly-skewed distributions, the median may be preferred to the mean.

The curve in Fig. 26 illustrates a distribution of particular importance. Its shape is often likened to that of a bell. It is precisely symmetrical about the measures of central tendency which here coincide. The curve progressively nears the horizontal, but never actually touches. It is one example of the *normal curve of distribution*. Different examples have different shapes, for dimensions reflect the mean and standard deviation of the data set for which it is drawn. In illustration, Fig. 27 gives three contrasting shapes. All are examples of the normal curve of distribution. In (a) standard deviation is small, so values are clustered close to the mean to give a tall thin 'bell'. In (c) the mean is the same as in (a), but standard deviation is larger. Values are more dispersed and the 'bell' has a more gentle outline.

It must be stressed that the normal curve of distribution is not 'normal' in the sense that it is the most common distribution. Rather, it is to be judged as a standard against which comparisons may be made. The perfect symmetry of the normal curve is seldom achieved, but many distributions show close approximations, especially when the number of values is large. Annual rainfall totals, the height of plant species, and particle size in deposited material, are three typical examples.

Although different in shape, the curves in Figs. 26 and 27, and indeed all instances of a normal distribution, have important properties in common. When distribution is truly normal, 68.27% of the values lie within a range of $\pm 1\sigma$ of the mean; 95.45% lie between $\pm 2\sigma$ of the mean, and 99.73% within $\pm 3\sigma$ of the mean. In practice, these clumsy figures are rounded off to 68%, 95% and 99%, and it is these simple figures that are used in Fig. 28. The area under the curve represents the total distribution, and because the curve is symmetrical it may be further subdivided as indicated. Note that less than 1% of values lie outside the limits of $\pm 3\sigma$.

These properties of the normal curve may be more readily appreciated in a less abstract form. Suppose a large sample of pebbles is selected at random from a shingle beach. The length of each pebble is found by measuring the longest axis. The mean is 8 cm and the standard deviation is 1.5 cm. The distribution of the values of length is found to be normal, and is pictured diagrammatically in Fig. 29, in which the horizontal axis is marked with symbolic divisions and the pebble length appropriate to this example. It will be appreciated from Fig. 29 that 68% of the pebbles will be between 6.5 cm and 9.5 cm in length; 95% will be between 5 cm and 11 cm and 99% will be between 3.5 cm and 12.5 cm.

Fig. 27 *Some examples of the normal curve of distribution*

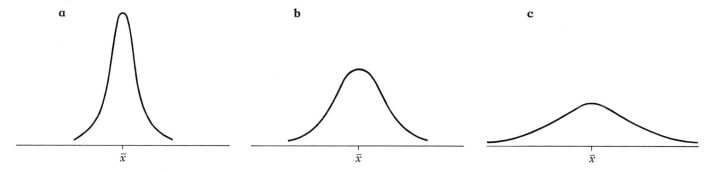

Fig. 28 *The properties of a normal curve of distribution*

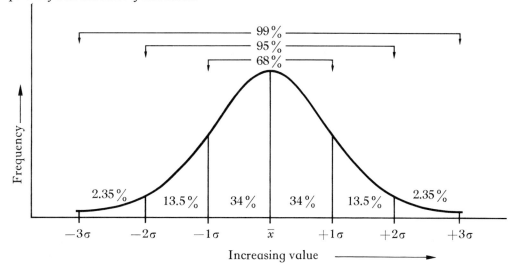

Fig. 29 *The normal distribution curve of the values of length of a sample of pebbles*

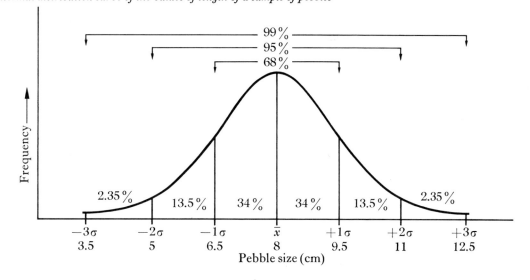

27 Consider the distribution illustrated by Fig. 29. If the sample had consisted of 100 pebbles, how many (approximately) would have been:
a between 6.5 cm and 9.5 cm;
b between 5 cm and 11 cm;
c between 5 cm and 6.5 cm;
d more than 9.5 cm in length?

28 The height of 200 specimens of a particular plant species was measured. The distribution of values was found to be perfectly normal. Mean height was 6.5 cm and standard deviation was 0.5 cm. How many specimens were:
a equal to or more than 6.5 cm;
b between 6 cm and 7 cm;
c between 5.5 cm and 6.5 cm;
d between 7 cm and 7.5 cm;
e less than 5.5 cm in height?

The same hypothetical sample of pebbles used in Fig. 29 will serve to illustrate another important point. Suppose that a friend secretly selects just one of the pebbles. There is no magical way of telling the length of this particular pebble, but knowing that distribution is normal, certain statements can be made. For instance, the chances are 50–50 that it is 8 cm or more in length. "Chances are" is layman's language. The statistician would say that there is 50% *probability* that the pebble is 8 cm or more in length. Probability that the length of the pebble is 8 cm or less is also 50%. Fig. 29 suggests other statements of probability that can be made. There is 68% probability that the length of the pebble is between 6.5 cm and 9.5 cm. The probability that the pebble is between 3.5 cm and 12.5 cm is 99%.

---

29 Using Fig. 29 state the probability of the length of a selected pebble being between:
a 8 cm and 11 cm;
b 5 cm and 8 cm;
c 3.5 cm and 9.5 cm.

30 Consider the data presented in question 28. State the probability that the height of a particular specimen is:
a equal to or more than 6.5 cm;
b between 6 cm and 7 cm;
c between 7 cm and 7.5 cm;
d between 5 cm and 5.5 cm;
e between 5.5 cm and 8 cm in height.

Probability, symbolised as p, may also be expressed as a decimal on a scale ranging from 0 to 1 as seen in Fig. 30. A probability of 1 is absolute certainty which is seldom, if ever, achieved. At $p = 0.99$, however, we come very close.

Probability may be viewed as a measure of our confidence in a conclusion. If the probability of a value lying within $\pm 1\sigma$ of the mean is 68%, then it follows that we can be 68% confident that this is so. Levels of probability are therefore termed *confidence levels*. The three in common use are listed in Fig. 31, which is completed for the pebble sample considered previously in Fig. 29. We have 68% confidence that a selected pebble will be between 6.5 cm and 9.5 cm in length. If 100 pebbles were selected and we quoted the above confidence limits on each occasion, we would be correct 68

Fig. 30 *The decimal scale of probability (p)*

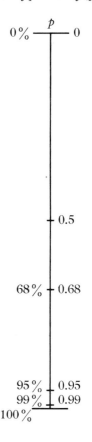

Fig. 31 *Confidence levels of pebble sample*

	Confidence level	Confidence limits	Confidence range
1	68%	6.5 – 9.5 cm	3
2	95%	5 – 11 cm	6
3	99%	3.5 – 12.5 cm	9

Fig. 32 *Table to compare the distribution of values in a data set with the normal curve*

Annual rainfall over 25 years in centimetres

Station B

	59	90	86	36	53	123	90	43	111	68
	74	79	99	58	73	38	120	60	68	77
	89	80	78	87	48					

$\bar{x} = 75.5 \quad \sigma = 22.9$

		Tally	Total	%	% under normal curve
-3σ	6.8				
			0	0	2.35
-2σ	29.7				
		√√ √√	4	16	13.5
-1σ	52.6				
		√√√√√√ √√	8	32	34
$\bar{x}$	75.5				
		√√√√√√√√√	9	36	34
$+1\sigma$	98.4				
		√√√	3	12	13.5
$+2\sigma$	121.3				
		√	1	4	2.35
$+3\sigma$	144.2				

$n = 25$

times. We would, of course, be wrong 32 times out of 100, thus the first confidence level is not very inspiring, and is seldom acceptable. At the 95% confidence level there are only 5 chances in 100 of error. We can feel much more secure in an answer, but Fig. 31 reveals that added confidence is only achieved at the cost of wider limits (that is, a wider *confidence range*). The third confidence level continues the trend. In many lines of geographical research, the 95% level is generally acceptable, but 99% is obviously preferred.

Probability has many practical applications. Water authorities, for instance, when planning new storage facilities, are greatly interested in the probability of annual precipitation exceeding or falling below certain selected totals. Rainfall at station B (referred to in Fig. 15) will serve as an example. For convenience, the data is reprinted in Fig. 32. The mean and standard deviation are quoted. The first step is to test the distribution for normality, and this can be done by comparison with the known properties of the normal distribution. A table is prepared as in Fig. 32. To the left, standard deviations are given the values appropriate to this example.

As a safeguard against counting errors, individual values are ticked in the appropriate box, the contents of which are then totalled and converted to a percentage of the total number of values. These figures can then be readily compared with those of the normal distribution recorded in the final column. In this example, the match is not exact. This is not surprising in view of the fact that the data set consists of only 25 values. It is likely that, had more values been available, resemblance would have been closer. In any event, the differences are only slight, and approximation is close enough to justify conclusions being drawn.

Fig. 33 *The normal distribution curve of rainfall at Station B*

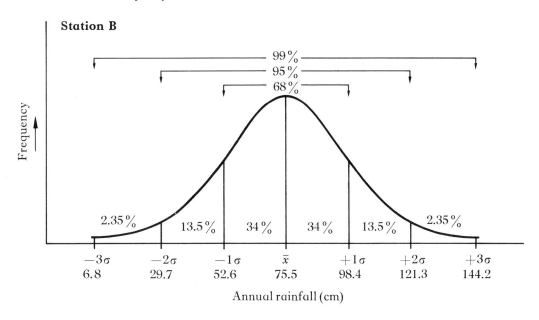

Drawn diagrammatically, the distribution is seen in Fig. 33, which suggests a variety of probability statements. The following are examples that may be checked with the aid of Fig. 33.

The probability of annual rainfall at station B being:
equal to or more than 75.5 cm is 50% ($p = 0.5$);
between 52.6 cm and 98.4 cm is 68% ($p = 0.68$);
more than 98.4 cm and less than 52.6 cm is 32% ($p = 0.32$);
more than 144.2 cm or below 6.8 cm is less than 1% ($p = <0.01$);
in excess of 98.4 cm is 16% (approx.) ($p = 0.16$);
less than 98.4 cm is 84% (approx.) ($p = 0.84$).

 Using Fig. 33, state the probability of rainfall at station B being:
a equal to or less than 75.5 cm;
b between 29.7 cm and 121.3 cm;
c less than 29.7 cm and more than 121.3 cm;
d less than 29.7 cm;
e more than 121.3 cm.

Often, the probability of annual precipitation exceeding a specific amount is required. In the case of station B, for instance, the water authority may need to know the probability of precipitation in any one year being greater than 110 cm, which is between 1σ and 2σ above the mean. To solve this problem the chosen figure, 110 cm, must be converted into a z-score. This, symbolised as z and pronounced zee, is found with the help of the formula:

$$z = \frac{x - \bar{x}}{\sigma}$$

Substitution gives

$$z = \frac{110 - 75.5}{22.9} = 1.5065$$

To one decimal place this gives a z-score of 1.5. If this is referred to the table (Fig. 34), it will be seen that with $z = 1.5$, the probability of rainfall exceeding 110 cm is 0.067 or approximately 7%. Annual precipitation in excess of 110 cm can be expected in seven years in every hundred.

Fig. 35 is visual representation. Use the formula to check that the z-score of the figures for centimetres is as quoted. The probability of rainfall exceeding 110 cm is represented by the shaded area under the curve and is, as we have seen, 7%. As the total area under the curve equals 100% probability, the probability of rainfall being less than 110 cm is $100 - 7 = 93\%$.

In similar fashion, the probability of annual precipitation being below a particular figure may be calculated. What is the probability of annual precipitation at station B being less than 40 cm?

22

The z-score is calculated from the formula:

$$z = \frac{40 - 75.5}{22.9} = -1.5502 = -1.6 \text{ (to 1 decimal place)}$$

Thus the z-score is -1.6. The sign is minus, but because the normal curve is symmetrical, the sign may be ignored, and the table used as described above. When $z = 1.6$, $p = 0.055$ (6% approx.). Thus annual precipitation of less than 40 cm is likely in six years in every hundred.

32 At station B, what is the probability of precipitation being:
a in excess of   i) 85 cm,   ii) 100 cm,   iii) 125 cm;
b below   i) 60 cm,   ii) 50 cm,   iii) 25 cm?

33 Test the data for annual precipitation at station A (Fig. 15, page 12), and, if distribution approximates to normal, calculate the probability of precipitation being:
a in excess of   i) 80 cm,   ii) 95 cm;
b below   i) 70 cm,   ii) 55cm.

Fig. 34 *z-score conversion table*

z	p	p as approx. %
0.0	0.500	50
0.1	0.460	46
0.2	0.421	42
0.3	0.382	38
0.4	0.345	35
0.5	0.309	31
0.6	0.274	27
0.7	0.242	24
0.8	0.212	21
0.9	0.184	18
1·0	0.159	16
1.1	0.136	14
1.2	0.115	12
1.3	0.097	10
1.4	0.081	8
1.5	0.067	7
1.6	0.055	6
1.7	0.045	5
1.8	0.036	4
1.9	0.029	3
2.0	0.023	2
2.1	0.018	2
2.2	0.014	1
2.3	0.011	1
2.4	0.008	1
2.5	0.006	1

When $z = >2.5, p = <1\%$

Fig. 35 *The z-score and the normal curve of distribution*

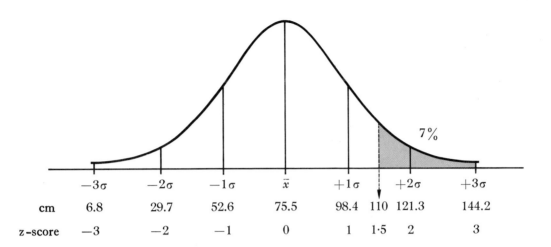

cm	6.8	29.7	52.6	75.5	98.4	110	121.3	144.2
z-score	−3	−2	−1	0	1	1·5	2	3

Consolidation

34 The height of 36 specimens of a moorland grass was measured. The measurements, to the nearest half centimetre, are given below.

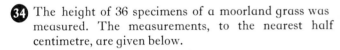

19.5	25.5	26	33.5	11	23	28	28
39	18	21	23	9.5	20	32	13
19.5	15.5	23	16.5	6.5	24.5	20.5	31
26	13	21	23.5	31	27.5	22.5	23
17	21.5	14.5	19				

a Calculate the mean, median and modal class of this data set.

b Determine the upper and lower quartiles, and state the interquartile range.

c Calculate the standard deviation.

d At a site some 150 metres higher, and with thinner, more acid soils, a similar sample of the same species was measured. The mean height was found to be 14.33 cm with a standard deviation of 7.1 cm. Compare these measures with the results obtained in **a** and **c** above, and write a brief interpretation.

e Illustrate the distribution of values within the data set by drawing:
   i) a dispersion diagram;
   ii) a histogram;
   iii) a frequency polygon;
   iv) a cumulative frequency curve (ogive).
   Comment on the relative merits of the four techniques.

f How close is the distribution of values in this data set to the normal distribution?

35 From the information provided by Fig. 127 (pages 88 and 89) produce, for each group of parishes, data of:
a cattle per 100 ha of farmland;
b sheep and lambs per 100 ha of farmland.
In each case, calculate the mean and the standard deviation, and use them in comparative description.

36 Analysis of annual rainfall totals (in centimetres) over a period of fifty years produced a mean of 42 with a standard deviation of 6. State the probability of annual rainfall being:
a   i) equal to or more than 42 cm,
   ii) between 36 and 48 cm,
   iii) more than 54 cm;
b   i) more than 50 cm,
   ii) less than 35 cm.

Section B · Sources of Statistics

The geographer can tap a variety of sources in his quest for the data needed to illuminate his studies.

Published Statistics

The details of area and population quoted in columns A and B of Fig. 2 (page 5) were extracted from the reports of the 1981 census, carried out by the Office of Population Censuses and Surveys. These reports, issued on a county basis, are a good example of a published data source. For the geographer they are a rich mine of valuable information. For units as small as parish or ward they record population and households in fine detail. For larger administrative units, a much wider range of data is presented. The first census was taken in 1801 and, with the solitary exception of 1941, the exercise has been repeated every ten years. Thus, there are opportunities for the study of change through time. The simple early censuses involved little more than the counting of heads, and so only population totals have the full historical perspective. In many cases, changes in administrative boundaries may pose problems.

Examination of the volumes which cover your local area will prove most rewarding. Copies are generally available in the reference section of central, if not branch, libraries; and other data source books will be found on neighbouring shelves. For the majority of those relating to the United Kingdom we are indebted to the Government Statistical Service. Typical examples are *The Digest of United Kingdom Energy Statistics*, *Regional Statistics*, and *United Kingdom Mineral Statistics*. A full list is available in a pamphlet entitled, *Government Statistics—a brief guide to sources*, which is available from Her Majesty's Stationery Office.

Information about foreign countries is not so readily available. A broad picture may be obtained from volumes compiled by the United Nations Organisation—its *Statistical Year-book*, for example. For more detailed data, the relevant embassy is perhaps the most hopeful line of enquiry.

Unpublished Statistics

Statistical information of specialist interest is collected by a variety of authorities and organisations. Often it lies unpublished—but not unavailable. The agricultural data given in Fig. 127 (pages 88 and 89) is a good example. In June each year, a detailed summary of farms and farming in each parish is completed. It includes details of crops and livestock, land use and landholdings. Farms are analysed by size, type and labour input. Copies of these parish summaries may be obtained, at small cost, from the Ministry of Agriculture, Fisheries and Food, Government Buildings, Epsom Road, Guildford, Surrey, GU1 2LD.

If interest lies in manufacturing or commerce, a letter to the appropriate trade association may prove fruitful. For your home area, a courteous approach to the local authority may yield informative unpublished data.

Maps

Maps present information in dimensions truly geographical. The Ordnance Survey (OS) map, in detail appropriate to its scale, highlights spatial variation in the physical landscape, and records the human response. Other map series add to the picture. The Geological Survey contributes coverage of solid rock and glacial drift. Land Use sheets are available for much of the country and the mapping of soils is proceeding. Maps generally tell their story in symbols, but simple techniques can unlock significant data, and so increase our understanding.

Fig. 36 *Bearings taken as the clockwise angular measurement from grid north*

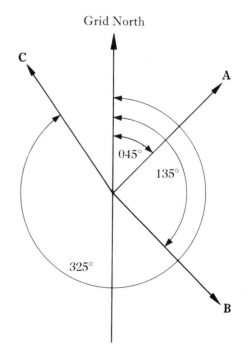

Orientation

Features recorded on the map frequently have a significant directional component. Orientation can, of course, be defined with points of the compass, but measurement of bearings gives the greater degree of precision that is usually desirable. An OS map's vertical grid lines serve as a convenient zero. Bearings are taken as the clockwise angular measurement from grid north. Fig. 36 gives three examples. The bearing of A is 045°. The same figure is its orientation. The orientation of B and C are 135° and 325° respectively. As bearings frequently exceed 180°, a circular protractor is a distinct advantage.

---

1 The sketch map shows a clutch of half a dozen cirques cleaving the flanks of a pyramidal peak. Trace the sketch and bisect each cirque to indicate orientation. Insert a convenient grid north parallel to the sides of the frame. A worked example is included. Find the approximate orientation of the remaining cirques.

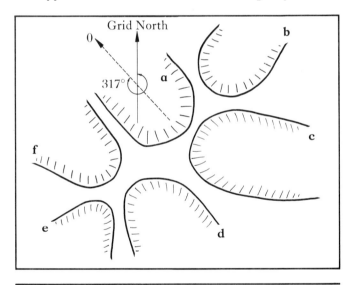

For linear features, the technique is similar. The elliptical shapes in Fig. 37 represent drumlins swarming south into a single valley. Two are selected as examples. The long axis is marked by a pecked line. Grid north is indicated by a line drawn parallel to the side of the map. Orientation is the clockwise angle between the two lines. Note that with linear features the maximum orientation is 179°.

---

2 Trace Fig. 37 and find the orientation of the remaining drumlins.

Fig. 37 *Orientation of linear landscape features*

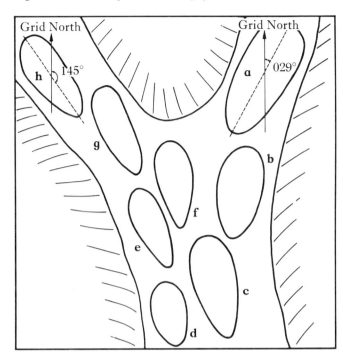

Area

Without the aid of expensive equipment it is impossible to measure exactly the area of the often complex shapes portrayed on a map. Fig. 38, however, illustrates a technique that yields adequate approximation. It represents (at a reduced scale) the outline of a lake under the grid of a 1 : 50 000 OS map. The area of each square is 1 km². Tracing paper is placed over the map. Each kilometre square that lies totally within the lake is ticked. For the remainder, estimates are made by eye. If the lake occupies

Fig. 38 *Using the grid of a map to find approximate area*

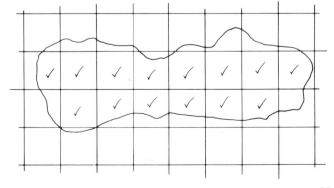

half or more of the square, it receives a tick. Squares with less than half are ignored. The sum of the ticks gives the approximate area. In this example it is 14 km².

The kilometre grid of the OS map is generally too coarse to provide an acceptable result when the area to be measured is small. But with the help of graph paper, the same technique can be applied with impressive accuracy. Fig. 39 shows a graph ruling in common use. The boldest lines are 2 cm apart. This distance on OS 1 : 50 000 maps represents 1 km. Thus bold squares, as at (a), are equivalent to 1 km². Subdivision, as indicated in (b), gives 0.25 km², and even 0.01 km². Thus graph paper provides squares representing a variety of areas. Which one to use will depend upon the degree of accuracy required and the time available. An adequate unit for most purposes is 0.25 km² and its use is featured in Fig. 39(c). The continuous line represents a tracing of the perimeter of an area of woodland. Ticks are awarded to all 0.25 km² squares where woodland cover is 50% or more. Ticks are counted. There are 22 squares each with an area of 0.25 km². The approximate area is 22 × 0.25 km² = 5.5 km².

With maps at scales other than 1 : 50 000, and with different graph rulings, the area value of the chosen square must be carefully determined. If the scale of the map represented in Fig. 39 was 1 : 25 000 on which 4 cm represent 1 km, the bold squares would have a value of 0.25 km².

---

3 Determine the area occupied by rough grazing on Fig. 52, page 34.

4 Calculate the area of land on Fig. 128, page 90, that is:
a below 100 metres;
b above 140 metres.

Fig. 39 *Using graph paper to find approximate area*

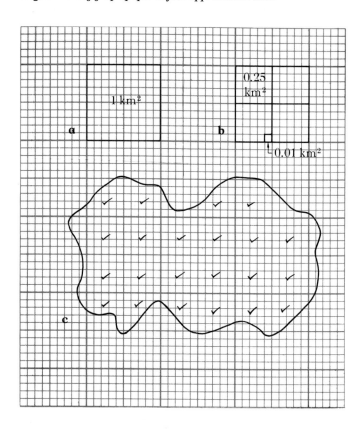

Shape

Brief examination of Fig. 1 (page 4) reveals the variety and complexity of shape adopted by rural parishes. A glance at any OS map reveals that the same is true of woodland, built-up areas, and many other features of the landscape. Shape is significant, yet words are a poor medium for description. They are vague and subjective and do not lend themselves to fine comparison. A means of expressing shape in mathematical form is therefore desirable. Several are available and one of the simplest (and by no means the least reliable), is illustrated with the help of Fig. 40. The shape is that of the parish of Forest and Frith. Axis A is the longest line that can be drawn within the area. From the mid-point of axis A, axis B is drawn at right angles. The map length of A is divided by that of B and the result is the *shape* (or *compactness*) *index*. In this example, 54 mm divided by 34 mm gives a shape index of 1.59.

Fig. 40 *The map length of axis A divided by that of B gives the shape index of the parish*

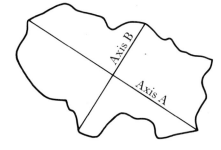

If this technique is applied to the neat, compact shape of a circle, the shape index is 1. The more elongated a shape, the higher the shape index. With shape thus expressed in mathematical terms, comparisons can be precise and meaningful.

5 Calculate the shape (compactness) index of the following pairs of parishes, (Fig. 130, page 93):
 a Middleton-in-Teesdale (3) and Lartington (12);
 b Eggleston (4) and Holwick (7);
 c Newbiggin (2) and Cotherstone (11).

6 Turn to Fig. 128, page 90. Compare the shapes of the areas of orchard centred on:
 a 2550; **b** 4525; **c** 7550.

Gradient and Slope

The topographical map plots position precisely and, within limits imposed by the contour interval, accurately reveals altitude. With position and height available, gradient—the slope of the land surface—may readily be calculated. Refer to Fig. 41. From A to B there is a gain of 29 m in 1.1 km. That is, 29 m in 1100 m. Gain in height must be reduced to unity, so both values are divided by 29. This gives 1 m in 38 m (to the nearest whole number). This, usually written 1 : 38, is the *gradient*.

The angle of slope can be found with the help of a right-angled triangle and simple trigonometry. In Fig. 42, the angle at A is the angle of slope. Its tangent is $\frac{29}{1100}$, which is 0.0264. This the tangent tables or calculator translates into an angle of 1.5°.

It must be remembered that slopes are seldom perfectly uniform over any significant distance, and gradients and angles derived from maps are *average* values.

Refer to Fig. 128, page 90.
7 Calculate the average gradient and the average angle of slope from:
 a 2080 to 2090;
 b 5050 to 5015.

A useful visual impression of the rise and fall of the land surface may be obtained by drawing a *section*. The contour sketch (Fig. 43) serves to illustrate the technique. A section is required along the line AB, and this distance becomes the baseline in Fig. 44, the scale of which is therefore the same as that of the map. Verticals, erected at each end of the baseline, carry the vertical scale which must be chosen with care. Too small a scale makes slopes imperceptible; with too large an interval, gentle knolls develop alpine proportions. Experiment may be necessary to find the scale most appropriate to the relief depicted on the map. The straight edge of a piece of paper is laid along the line of section and contour position and values are neatly noted. When the paper is transferred to the baseline, position may readily be dotted against height. Dots are joined with a smooth curve.

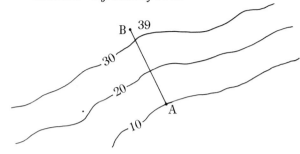

Fig. 41 *From A to B there is a gain in height of 29 metres in 1.1 kilometres—a gradient of 1 : 38*

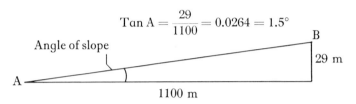

Fig. 42 *Calculating the angle of slope of line AB shown in Fig. 41*

$$\text{Tan A} = \frac{29}{1100} = 0.0264 = 1.5°$$

Fig. 43 *A simple contour sketch. A section is required along the line AB. This distance becomes the baseline of the section (Fig. 44)*

Scale 1 : 50 000 (1 cm : 500 m)

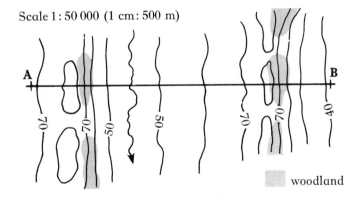

▨ woodland

Fig. 44 *A section along the line AB shown in Fig. 43. Note that horizontal and vertical scales are not the same. Sections always exaggerate the angle of slope*

Vertical scale 1 cm : 100 m

West   East

A   Horizontal scale 1cm : 500 m   B

VE = 5

Note that horizontal and vertical scales are not the same. Sections always exaggerate the angle of slope. In the above example, 1 cm represents 500 m on the horizontal scale, but only 100 m on the vertical. Thus, elevation is magnified five times. The vertical exaggeration (VE) is 5. This should be quoted on all sections.

Height and slope are, of course, vital elements in the landscape and influence the distribution of many natural and human phenomena. The section is the basis of the illustrative device known as a *transect*. Fig. 45 repeats the section from Fig. 44. The bar above records the position of the woodland that occurs along the line of section. The shading is positioned by direct measurement. This simple example suggests an association between woodland and steep slopes.

Fig. 45 *A transect to locate the woodland along the line AB of the contour sketch (Fig. 43)*

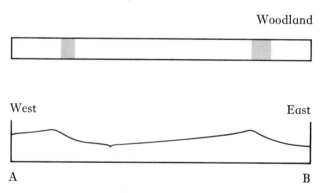

The transect is preferably drawn to cut the grain of relief, as indicated by clustered contours, at right angles. It can carry a variety of information. The location of vegetation, settlement, communications and so forth can be located by shading, words, or symbols. Details of soil and geology can be added from the relevant map series. A well-drawn, detailed transect can serve as a useful visual summary, but it must be remembered that it relates only to one particular line of section. A line only a short distance away may well give a somewhat different impression. Transects drawn as a result of field survey may be similarly used to record information and to illustrate relationships.

8 Refer to Fig. 128, page 90.
Draw a transect to indicate land use from north to south along grid line 3. Calculate the vertical exaggeration of your section.

Point Patterns

Many significant landscape features occupy relatively small areas of land. Villages and farms, factories and shops are four common examples. On a map, their distribution may be indicated by dots or points. Spatial distribution is of profound interest to the geographer, but description and comparison of *point patterns* poses particular problems. Standard adjectives, such as those illustrated by Fig. 46, may be applied, but words are inadequate for the accurate description of the subtleties of most real-life distributions. Happily, a precise mathematical means of description is available in *nearest-neighbour analysis*.

Fig. 46 *Illustration of distributions*

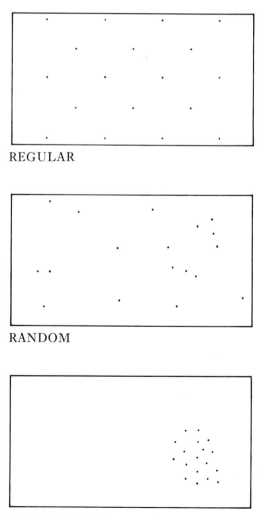

REGULAR

RANDOM

CLUSTERED

Nearest-Neighbour Analysis

A worked example will illustrate the method. Fig. 47 represents the distribution of villages in part of the English lowlands. It was achieved by placing tracing paper over the map and marking with a dot the centre of each village, but scale has been changed to meet constraints imposed by the size of the page. The frame, by convention, is the smallest rectangle that will hold the distribution.

Each dot, distinguished by number, is treated in sequence, and the distance between it and its nearest neighbour is carefully measured and recorded. Measurement need not be too arduous. Rotation of a pair of dividers quickly locates the nearest neighbour, and the same instrument, in co-operation with the linear scale speedily provides the distance. Distances, tabled as in Fig. 48, are totalled, and division by the number of dots (n) gives the mean distance ($\bar{d}$). Area (a) is measured in units matching those used for distances, that is km². The nearest-neighbour statistic (Rn) is obtained by substitution in the formula

$$Rn = 2\bar{d}\sqrt{\frac{n}{a}}$$

In the example, $\bar{d} = 1.63$, $n = 30$ and $a = 132$ km², thus

$$Rn = 3.26\sqrt{\frac{30}{132}}$$
$$= 3.26\sqrt{0.227}$$
$$= 3.26 \times 0.476$$
$$= 1.55$$

To interpret this result, reference is made to Fig. 49. From the vertical axis, it will be appreciated that the Rn statistic falls within a range of 0 to 2.15. An *Rn* value of 2.15 indicates a perfectly regular distribution. With an *Rn* value of 0, distribution is a hypothetically perfect clustering—that is, all points in a distribution have a common location. An *Rn* of 1 indicates a random distribution, and it is against this standard that comparisons are made. Because of the possibility of a random distribution being due to chance, values of *Rn* must fall outside the shaded area in Fig. 49 before a significant element of regularity or clustering can be accepted. Values falling within the shaded area indicate (at the 95% probability level) a random distribution. Note from Fig. 49 that significance increases with the value of *n*. Thirty points is the preferred minimum.

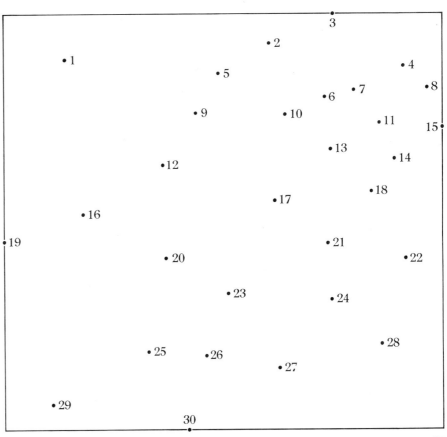

Fig. 47 *A distribution of villages in part of the English lowlands*

Fig. 48 *Table to calculate the mean distance*

Fig. 49 *Interpretation of Rn statistic*

Village no.	Nearest-neighbour	Distance (km)
1	9	3.8
2	5	1.6
3	2	1.9
4	8	0.9
5	9	1.2
6	7	0.8
7	6	0.8
8	4	0.9
9	5	1.2
10	6	1.1
11	14	1.0
12	9	1.7
13	6	1.4
14	11	1.0
15	8	1.1
16	19	2.3
17	21	1.9
18	14	1.1
19	16	2.3
20	23	2.0
21	24	1.5
22	18	2.0
23	26	1.8
24	21	1.5
25	26	1.6
26	25	1.6
27	26	2.1
28	24	1.8
29	25	3.0
30	26	2.0

$$\Sigma = 48.9 \text{ km} \qquad \bar{d} = \frac{48.9}{30} = 1.63 \text{ km}$$

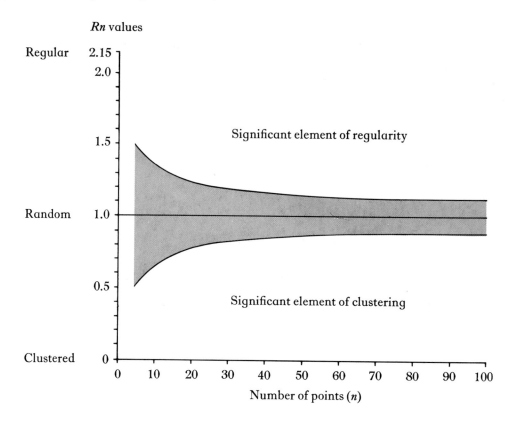

Fig. 49 reveals that in the example worked above, where $Rn = 1.55$, the distribution of villages has a modest but significant element of regularity. $Rn = 1.55$ is a precise description of the distribution.

The Rn statistic is useful when comparing two or more distributions. Suppose for instance that the distribution of villages in a second area was treated to nearest-neighbour analysis and the result was $Rn = 1.79$. Comparison of results indicates that both distributions show a significant degree of regularity, but the distribution in the second area is the more pronounced. Comparisons over time are also possible. The analysis of present and former patterns of the same feature will give an accurate measure of changing distribution. Nearest-neighbour analysis has further merit in that it frequently suggests profitable lines of geographical

investigation. Any distribution that shows a significant degree of clustering or regularity immediately prompts the question, "Why ?".

Nearest-neighbour analysis is a useful statistical method for the geographer, but it must be used with caution to avoid pitfalls. It is important that the feature to be investigated is precisely defined. This may not be easy with settlement, for instance, for settlement terms are notoriously vague. Hamlets merge imperceptibly into villages which grade slowly into towns. In preparing Fig. 47, the provision of services provided a useful yardstick. Each small settlement with an inn or a post office as well as a church was deemed to merit a dot.

In nearest-neighbour analysis, care must also be taken to obtain the total distribution of the feature to be investigated. For this, the published map may not be adequate. Farms, a tempting subject for analysis, are a case in point. There are ten farms in the parish of Raby with Keverstone, but on the 1 : 50 000 OS map, only two are identified by name. The map must often be supported by other sources of information.

In nearest-neighbour analysis, boundaries are most significant. The Rn statistic must be interpreted in the context of the area under investigation. Administrative units, geological outcrops and land below a certain altitude are three that may, depending on circumstances, be considered relevant and appropriate. In urban studies, the edge of the built-up area, or the limits of the Central Business District are obvious possibilities. Problems arise when the distribution does not have easily defined limits such as those suggested above. Fig. 47 is a case in point. It gives but a part of a much larger distribution—that of village settlement in the whole of the English lowlands. The nearest-neighbour of village 1 may not in fact be village 9, but a village outside the arbitrary frame, and the same is true of other points on the periphery of the distribution. Had a slightly larger area been chosen, the *Rn* statistic could well have been different. Fig. 50 dramatises the problem. Points are regularly spaced within square A, but if area is enlarged to square B, the pattern is decidedly clustered. Happily, such a dramatic situation is seldom encountered in practice, and providing the danger is borne in mind when selecting the study area, nearest-neighbour analysis gives useful and significant results.

Fig. 50 *In nearest-neighbour analysis, boundaries are most significant. The points are regularly spaced within square A, but if the area is enlarged to square B, the pattern is decidedly clustered*

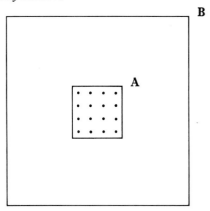

9 Apply the technique of nearest-neighbour analysis to the pattern of farms seen in Fig. 128, page 90. Interpret your answer with the aid of Fig. 49.

10 The map represents an area of 15.25 km² served by an inner city fire station. Calls answered over a three-day period in March 1981 are shown by dots. Calculate, and interpret, the nearest-neighbour statistic.

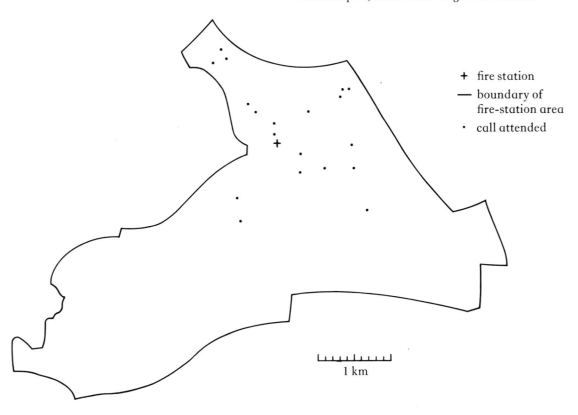

+ fire station
— boundary of fire-station area
· call attended

1 km

11 The map locates all farms making Cheshire cheese in:
a 1965 and 1975; **b** 1965 only.
Use nearest-neighbour analysis to determine if the decline in numbers resulted in any significant change in the pattern of distribution.

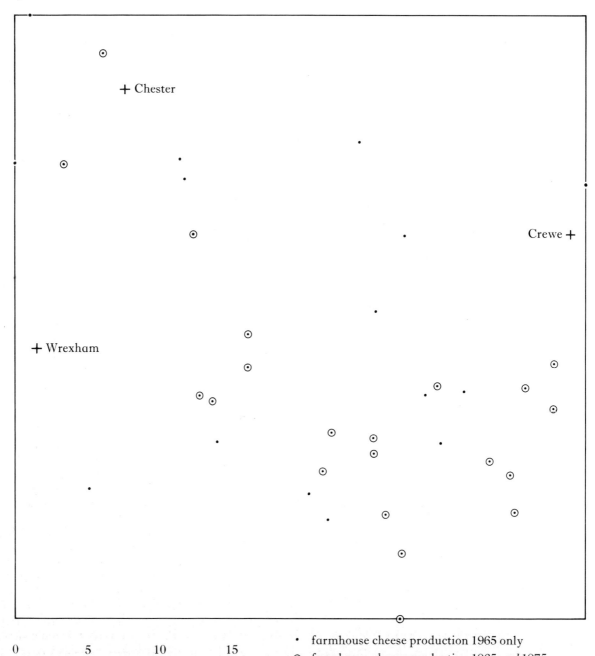

    0   5   10   15

km

•   farmhouse cheese production 1965 only

⊙   farmhouse cheese production 1965 *and* 1975

Fig. 51 *Mean centre of a point distribution*

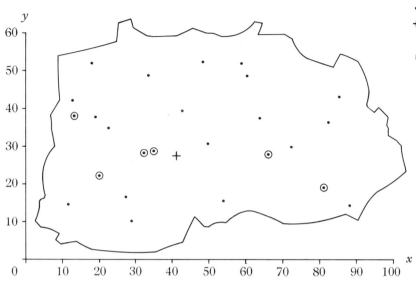

⊙ secondary school
· primary school
+ mean centre of distribution of secondary schools

1 km

Co-ordinates of secondary schools

x	y
13	38
20	22
32	28
35	29
66	28
81	19

$\Sigma x = 247$ $\Sigma y = 164$

$\bar{x} = 41.2$ $\bar{y} = 27.3$

Mean Centre

This is a further technique appropriate to point distributions. Fig. 51 will serve to illustrate. It outlines the built-up area of a suburb of a major conurbation. The distribution of secondary and primary schools is indicated by circles and dots respectively.

From a convenient origin to the south-west of the area, the map is given x and y axes. From Fig. 51, the distribution of secondary schools is selected as an example. Co-ordinates are found for each secondary school. The means of both sets of co-ordinates are calculated, and these mean co-ordinates are used to locate the *mean centre* of the distribution (indicated by + in Fig. 51).

The mean centre is a useful indication of the 'centre of gravity' of a distribution. Comparison between different distributions may readily be made, and changes with time can be illustrated.

12 Calculate the mean centre of the distribution of:
a the primary schools located on Fig. 51;
b the farms in Fig. 128, page 90.

13 The map in question 11 locates all farms making Cheshire cheese in: **a** 1965 and 1975; **b** 1965 only. Did the decline in numbers result in any change in the mean centre of the distribution?

Sampling

It is a fortunate geographer who finds that the information required falls readily to hand in figures or maps. In many investigations the collection of essential data is a truly formidable challenge. Take, for instance, the student wishing to study farming in Teesdale.

Ideally, the student would like information about every farm in the district, but as there are 818 of them, the task of visiting all may well be beyond his or her resources. A study of coastal processes might suggest the measurement of every pebble on a beach. Such a task is clearly impossible, as would be the counting of the number of specimens of the various species of plant which grow on a moorland hillside. These are but three examples of possible lines of research where the gathering of complete data is either too time-consuming or downright impossible. It is in situations such as these that the values of sampling techniques will be appreciated.

Farms in Teesdale, pebbles on a beach, plants on a hillside, all represent statistical *populations*. A selection made from one of these populations is a *sample population*. From observations of the sample it is possible to draw significant conclusions about the parent population. It must be stressed at the outset, however, that sampling never gives an answer of precise accuracy. It can, however, provide the best possible estimate, and this is adequate for many purposes. In sampling there are precautions to be taken and limitations to be recognised. Sampling has applications in many

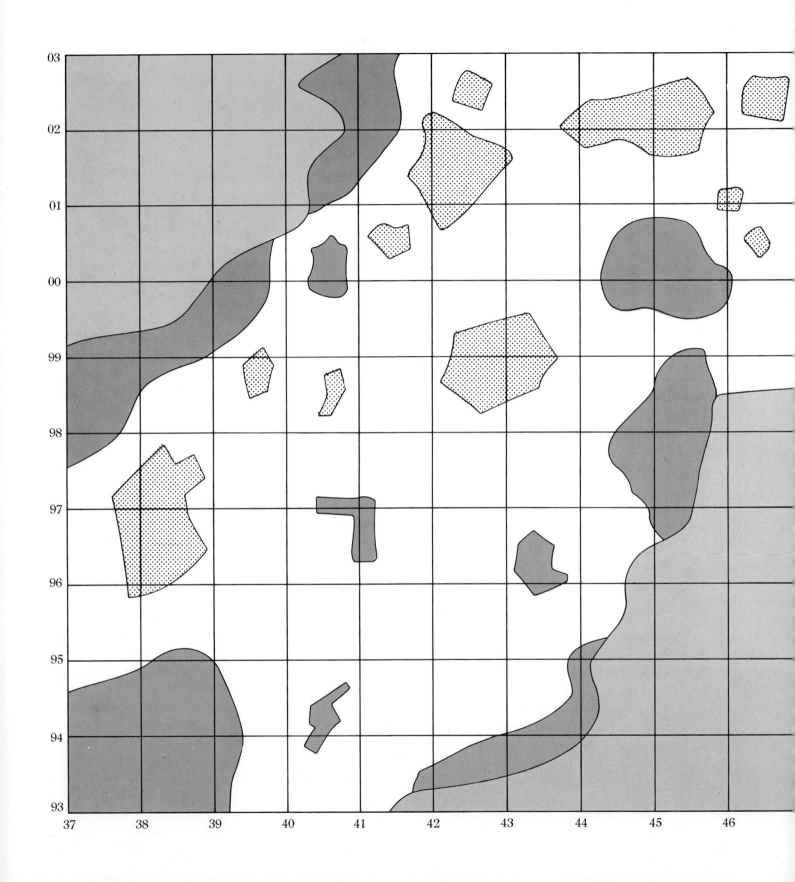

Fig. 52 *Sketch map of land use*

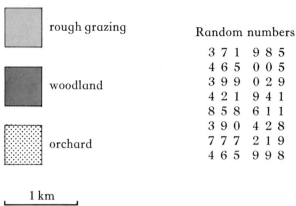

Random numbers

```
3 7 1   9 8 5
4 6 5   0 0 5
3 9 9   0 2 9
4 2 1   9 4 1
8 5 8   6 1 1
3 9 0   4 2 8
7 7 7   2 1 9
4 6 5   9 9 8
```

rough grazing

woodland

orchard

1 km

Fig. 53 *Table for recording random point sampling*

Rough grazing		Woodland		Orchard		Other	
Tally	%	Tally	%	Tally	%	Tally	%
✓✓✓✓✓ ✓✓✓✓✓ ✓✓✓✓✓ ✓✓✓✓✓ ✓✓✓✓✓ ✓✓✓✓ ✓	30/100 30%	✓✓✓✓✓ ✓✓✓✓✓ ✓✓✓✓✓ ✓✓✓✓✓ ✓	21/100 21%	✓✓✓✓✓ ✓✓✓✓✓ ✓✓	12/100 12%	✓✓✓✓✓ ✓✓✓✓✓ ✓✓✓✓✓ ✓✓✓✓✓ ✓✓✓✓✓ ✓✓✓✓✓ ✓✓✓✓✓ ✓✓	37/100 37%

$n = 100$

lines of research, but the techniques as applied to maps will serve to illustrate the basic principles.

Fig. 52 represents a small extract from the 1:50 000 OS map. The distribution of rough grazing, woodland, and orchard is indicated by shading. We wish to determine the percentage of land devoted to each of these three types of land use.

There are several methods of sampling, but the most appropriate in this case is known as *random point sampling*. The map is regarded as a population of points of infinite size. It is from this that we take the sample.

The first decision to be taken is the number of points to be selected. Thirty is generally regarded as the minimum. As explained below, accuracy increases with the size of the sample, but only at the cost of increased effort. Thus, in every case, the size of the sample is a compromise between the degree of accuracy required, and the time and patience available.

Sampling is most reliable when the selection of points is completely random. This means that every point on the map should have an equal chance of being selected. There must be no bias. The most convenient way of achieving this is by the use of *random number tables*. An example, Fig. 129, occupies page 92 and it merits close examination. Random number tables are produced by computer, and there is no significance whatsoever in the arrangement of digits. They are printed in blocks, merely as a matter of convenience to the user. Movement left or right along the rows, or up or down the columns, always provides a completely random sequence of digits.

To relate random numbers to points on the map, normal grid references are employed. Sets of six digits are therefore required—three for the easting and three for the northing. To generate the numbers required, a starting-point on the

table is selected at random. For purposes of illustration, let it be the number 3 that starts the second row in Fig. 129. Direction of movement is a matter of choice, but reading to the right and ignoring the spaces the first group of six is 376367, the second is 948469, and the third is 101569. Check with the table that the sequence continues 112144, 068959, 695358. At the end of a row (or column) we start on the next—no digits are missed. If selection should happen to generate two identical groups of digits, the second is simply ignored.

Turn again to Fig. 52. Assume that the figures printed with the key have been correctly extracted from a random number table. Take each in turn. Of the first, 371 is the easting and 985 is the northing. When the point is located on the map, it is seen to lie within an area of woodland, and this fact is ticked in a recording table such as the one suggested in Fig. 53. The number 465005 coincides with orchards, and 399029 with rough pasture. 421941 falls in none of the specified categories of land use and is ticked in the box reserved for 'others'. 858611 does not fall within the map and is rejected. So, too, are the two that follow. The last number, 465998, falls into the category marked 'others'. On a small map there is inevitably a high rejection rate. This is irritating and time-consuming, but must be patiently accepted. It helps if colleagues can be enlisted to generate the random numbers and record the results. In Fig. 53 ticks have been totalled and the totals converted into percentages.

It is tempting, but dangerous, to accept these figures as the required answer. It is perfectly true that rough grazing was located at 30% of the sample points, but it is not possible to assume that this figure is a true reflection of the parent population. Chance may have played a part. However, it is possible to calculate the limits within which the true answer must lie—at the three levels of confidence (page 20). For this it is necessary first of all to determine the *standard error* (SE), which bears a family resemblance to standard deviation. At the first level of confidence (68%) a value true for the parent population will lie within a range of $\pm$ 1SE of the sample value. Similarly, at the 95% and 99% confidence levels, the range will be $\pm$ 2SE and $\pm$ 3SE respectively.

When, as in the above example, the data is binomial, that is, the data can be placed in one of two mutually exclusive categories, standard error is obtained from the formula:

$$SE = \sqrt{\frac{p \times q}{n}}$$

where n = number of points in sample
p = % of points in one category
q = % of points *not* in this category.

In Fig. 53, rough grazing claims 30%; therefore, 70% is *not* rough grazing. With substitution:

$$SE = \sqrt{\frac{30 \times 70}{100}}$$
$$= \sqrt{\frac{2100}{100}}$$
$$= \sqrt{21}$$
$$= 4.58$$

Knowing the sample percentage (30) and the SE (4.58), we are in a position to make statements, relevant to the levels of confidence, about the true percentage of rough grazing within the map area. Fig. 54 provides a summary. Thus, we can state, with 99% confidence (that is, the risk of error being only one chance in a hundred) that the true percentage of rough grazing is between 16.26% and 43.74%. Similarly, at the 68% confidence level we can state that the true percentage is between 25.42% and 34.58%.

---

(14) Produce a table, similar to Fig. 54, for the sample percentages in Fig. 53 for:
a woodland;
b orchard.

Fig. 54 *Confidence level and confidence limits*

Rough grazing, sample % = 30

Confidence level	SE	Confidence limits
68%	4.58	30% $\pm$ 1SE (4.58) = 25·42% − 34.58%
95%	4.58	30% $\pm$ 2SE (9.16) = 20·84% − 39.16%
99%	4.58	30% $\pm$ 3SE (13.74) = 16·26% − 43.74%

The problem mentioned above, namely the high rejection rate when using six-figure random numbers with small maps, may in certain circumstances be solved by preparing a 10 by 10 grid on a tracing overlay. With both sets of grid lines numbered from 0 to 9, points may be located by four-figure rather than six-figure random numbers, and all will fall within the map area.

A further glance at Fig. 54 will highlight one difficulty often encountered with sampling exercises. At the 95% confidence level, the one that is generally found acceptable, the range of values is nearly 20%. This may well be too broad to be useful. Range depends on standard error, which is obviously influenced by n, the size of the sample. The larger the value of n, the smaller the standard error, and hence the tighter the confidence limits. Thus, more precise results can be achieved at the cost of a larger sample.

Fig. 55 provides illustration. It assumes that a sample percentage of 30 is achieved with samples of varying size. Standard error is given and confidence limits appropriate to the 95% confidence level are also quoted. It is clear from the figure how accuracy increases with the size of sample. Note, however, that accuracy increases at a decreasing rate. The small improvement resulting from sampling 400 rather than 300 points is unlikely to be worth the extra effort involved.

Fig. 55 *Accuracy increases with the size of the sample but at a decreasing rate*

Rough grazing, sample % = 30

Sample size n	Standard error SE	Confidence limits at 95% confidence level
30	8.37	13.26% − 46.74%
100	4.58	20.84% − 39.16%
200	3.24	23.52% − 36.48%
300	2.65	24.70% − 35.30%
400	2.29	25.42% − 34.58%

---

(15) Produce a table similar to Fig. 55 for sample percentages of:
a 21%; **b** 12%.

The formula for standard error used above is only appropriate to binomial data. When sampling is concerned with interval data—that is, actual values rather than frequency of occurrence—the essential calculation of standard error is a little less straightforward. Ideally, it is found by dividing the standard deviation of the parent population (σ) by the square root of the number of items in the sample:

$$SE = \frac{\sigma}{\sqrt{n}}$$

In a sampling situation, however, the value of σ is unobtainable but, if distribution is reasonably normal and n is greater than 30, the standard deviation of the sample data (distinguished as s) gives a close approximation. Therefore, s can take the place of σ, and the formula:

$$SE = \frac{s}{\sqrt{n}}$$

gives a result of acceptable accuracy.

Examine Fig. 56 for illustration. This records the bare bones of a random point sampling exercise designed to find the mean altitude of a small area selected from the 1:50 000 map. The layout of the table facilitates the recording of data and calculation of standard deviation (page 10). In this example the value of s was found to be 40.66, and with substitution in the formula:

$$SE = \frac{s}{\sqrt{n}}$$

$$SE = \frac{40.66}{\sqrt{50}}$$

$$SE = \frac{40.66}{7.07}$$

$$SE = 5.75$$

Thus, it can be said that at the 68% level of confidence the mean height of the area under investigation lies between 124.25 m and 135.75 m. With 95% confidence it can be stated that the mean height is between 118.5 m and 141.5 m.

Fig. 56 *Table for calculating the standard deviation of a sample (s)*

	Random number	Height above sea-level to nearest 10 metres	$x - \bar{x}$	$(x - \bar{x})^2$
1	395119	210	80	6400
2	369008	80	−50	2500
50	413095	140	10	100

$n = 50$ $\Sigma = 6500$ $\Sigma = 82\,650$
$\bar{x} = 130$

$$s = \sqrt{\frac{\Sigma (x - \bar{x})^2}{n}}$$

$$s = \sqrt{\frac{82\,650}{50}}$$

$$s = \sqrt{1653}$$

$$s = 40.66$$

Other Sampling Methods

Random point is the most favoured method of sampling from maps, but there are alternatives which may be preferred in particular circumstances. *Random square* is illustrated in Fig. 57. Four-figure random numbers provide co-ordinates for the squares selected. In Fig. 57 the selected squares, reading from left to right, have co-ordinates of 3721, 3922 and 4119 respectively. This method is often useful in the investigation of linear features such as drainage channels or lines of communication, where measurement over large areas can be burdensome.

A third possibility is *random line* sampling, illustrated by Fig. 58 which represents part of an OS map. Note that the top and right-hand side have been given a contrasting sequence of numbers. Each sample line is drawn between points on the frame selected by random numbers, three for

Fig. 57 *Random square sampling*

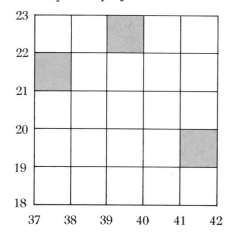

Fig. 58 *Random line sampling*

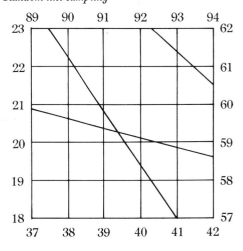

the starting-point and three for the terminus. The lines in Fig. 58 relate to 895410, 923605 and 209586. The number of lines is a matter of choice. A greater number yields greater accuracy, at the cost of increased effort. The length of, say, woodland along each of the lines is carefully measured and totalled. This can then be expressed as a percentage of the total length of line.

Random sampling, by ensuring that every item in the parent population has an equal chance of selection, successfully avoids bias and returns reliable results. It can, however, be highly demanding of time and patience.

Systematic sampling offers an alternative which is much less demanding. It is evident from Fig. 59 that grid intersections provide a ready-made, equally-spaced, systematic selection of points. These points may be used for sampling in exactly the same way as points generated at random. Similarly, northings or eastings can be used in the same way as random lines. Fig. 59 shades one of many possible patterns of systematic squares.

The speed and convenience of systematic sampling, be it point, line or square, is much appreciated. Moreover, the accuracy of the result is often comparable to that achieved by random methods. There are dangers, however, and one is illustrated by Fig. 60. Shading represents woodland, which, like many landscapes features, often has a linear shape. It is clear that systematic point sampling would give an odd result. Instances such as this, though admittedly not common, suggest that systematic sampling is less worthy of trust, and that the greater effort involved in random methods is generally justified.

Stratified sampling is a refinement of considerable value in geographical studies. Consider Fig. 61 which represents the pattern of woodland over an area consisting of two contrasting parts. In this case the difference is geological. It could just as easily be a reflection of altitude, soil or slope. The sampling techniques considered above will readily yield a figure for the percentage of woodland over the area as a whole, but this shirks the question of spatial distribution.

Fig. 59 *Systematic sampling*

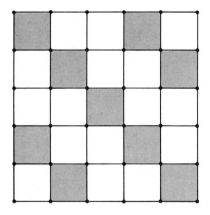

Fig. 60 *A shortcoming of systematic sampling*

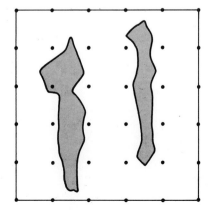

Fig. 61 *Stratified sampling*

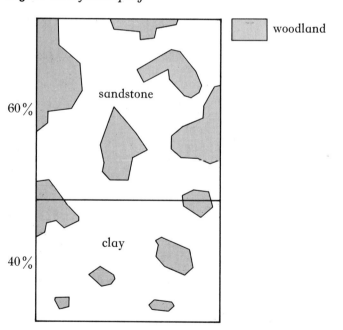

Does the percentage of woodland vary with rock type? Stratified sampling will suggest an answer.

Assume a random sample of 100 points. Sandstone occupies 60% of the map area, and thus has a quota of 60 points. Clay has a quota of 40. Points are located by random numbers in the usual way. If more than a quota is generated, the surplus is ignored. The occurrence of woodland is

Fig. 62 *Table to record results of stratified sampling*

	Woodland		Others	
	Tally	%	Tally	%
Sandstone	✓✓✓ ✓ ✓ ✓ ✓✓ ✓ ✓ ✓✓ ✓✓✓✓ ✓✓ ✓ ✓✓✓✓✓	$\frac{23}{60}$ 38%	✓ ✓ ✓✓ ✓✓ ✓✓ ✓ ✓ ✓✓ ✓✓✓✓✓ ✓ ✓ ✓✓ ✓✓✓✓ ✓ ✓✓	$\frac{37}{60}$
Clay	✓✓✓✓ ✓ ✓	$\frac{6}{40}$ 15%	✓✓ ✓✓ ✓✓✓✓ ✓ ✓ ✓✓ ✓✓✓✓ ✓✓ ✓✓ ✓ ✓✓✓ ✓ ✓	$\frac{34}{40}$

recorded separately for each area as indicated in Fig. 62, from which it will be appreciated that subject to consideration of standard error and confidence limits, woodland is markedly more prevalent on sandstone than it is on clay. This result could well stimulate a quest for explanation.

Other Sampling Situations

In preceding paragraphs, exclusive use has been made of maps to illustrate the principles of sampling. The same principles may readily be applied to other situations in which the geographer seeks his data. Three examples will give an indication of the possibilities.

1. In a study of manufacturing in a major industrial centre, the mean factory size, as measured by the number of employees, is considered to be important. This information is available only at the cost of a personal visit, but the expense and effort involved in visiting all the factories in the region is clearly prohibitive. If, however, a list of factories can be obtained, a sample may easily be selected for investigation. Systematically, this could be done by taking names from the list at regular intervals — five, ten or whatever will provide a sample of the required size. If random selection is preferred, the list is numbered in sequence and appropriate digits are taken from the random number tables. The data is then obtained from the selected factories and this can be processed for standard error, and the results expressed to an acceptable level of confidence. The technique of sampling from lists is fitting to many lines of research. It is simple and straightforward and, provided that the list is complete and up to date, it gives results of rewarding accuracy.

2. Sampling has many applications in geomorphology. Assume that the object of study is a shingle beach. The size and shape of the pebbles may well cast some light on the processes at work. It is clearly impossible to measure them all, and sampling is therefore a relevant technique. The inland edge of the beach is a possible baseline. It can be measured quite adequately by pacing with a regular step. Points on this baseline are selected systematically or at random. At these points, measuring tapes are extended at right angles to the baseline. Tapes are convenient for sampling. A 20-metre tape holds 2000 cm, and random numbers (four digits) can identify individual centimetre marks. Pebbles found at the selected marks can be measured and the results recorded. In this case the mean size and shape of the pebbles for the beach as a whole will be of limited significance, but variation in the mean at different parts of the beach may be thought-provoking. It may be added that random number tables are not easy to manipulate in drizzling rain or a north-east gale, and the prior preparation of suitable lists is highly advisable.

3. In many investigations the only convenient way to obtain required data is by stopping people in the street and asking questions. This popular questionnaire technique is, of course, a form of sampling, but one in which sampling safeguards are often overlooked. Questions must be chosen with care. They must be few in number and designed to yield simple, factual, relevant answers.

It is often difficult to avoid bias in the selection of the sample population to be questioned. Choice must be avoided. It is tempting to ignore a fearsome prospect and plump instead for a charming person of the opposite sex. When a questionnaire has been completed and the victim thanked, it must be offered to the next person that chances to pass. In assessing results, the nature of the population must be borne in mind. If the questions were asked on a wet Tuesday afternoon in February, it is a sample of the population who happened to be out and about at such a time and in such weather conditions. It may, or, more likely, may not, be representative of the total population.

Consolidation

16 From Fig. 128, page 90, determine the area of land which is:
   a over 180 m;
   b below 80 m;
   c between 100 m and 200 m above sea-level.

17 From Fig. 131, page 94, calculate the shape (compactness) index of the parishes of:
   a Streatlam and Stainton (30);
   b Staindrop (31).

18 a Use the nearest-neighbour technique to describe the distribution of post offices in:
i) Teesdale parishes group A and ii) Teesdale parishes group B, as indicated on Figs. 130, and 131, pages 93 and 94.
b In the light of experience gained from this and other exercises, comment critically on the value of nearest-neighbour analysis.

19 Consider Fig. 128, page 90. Use **a.** random point and **b.** systematic point sampling techniques to find the percentage area devoted to:
i) woodland;
ii) orchard.
In each case calculate the standard error, and present your answer in terms appropriate to the three levels of confidence.

20 Refer to Fig. 52, page 34. By **a.** random point and **b.** systematic point methods, determine for the 95% confidence level the percentage of land *not* devoted to rough grazing, woodland or orchard.

21 Use **a.** random point and **b.** systematic point sampling techniques to determine at the 95% confidence level the mean height of the land mapped in Fig. 128, page 90.

22 Comment on the relative merits of random and systematic point sampling methods.

23 Design sampling exercises to determine:
a the length of A and B class roads in the area covered by a sheet of the OS 1:50 000 map;
b the mean width of the floor of a major valley, and the mean height of its sides;
c the relative importance of selected plant species in a small area of moorland;
d possible variation in fragment size on a scree slope;
e variations in agricultural land use around a market town.

Section C · Data in Harness

Fig. 63 *Climatic data for a selection of German meteorological stations*

No.	Station	Lat. N (to nearest 15′)	Long. E	Mean July temp. (°C)	Mean Jan. temp. (°C)	Annual range of temp. (°C)	Precipitation (mm)
1	Bielefeld	52° 00′	8° 30′	16.9	0.7	16.2	839
2	Brunswick	52° 15′	10° 30′	17.6	0.2	17.4	676
3	Hanover	52° 15′	9° 45′	17.6	0.2	17.4	637
4	Magdeburg	52° 15′	11° 45′	17.7	−0.3	18.0	506
5	Osnabrück	52° 15′	8° 00′	17.1	1.1	16.0	887
6	Potsdam	52° 30′	13° 00′	18.1	−0.7	18.8	585
7	Bremen	53° 00′	8° 45′	17.4	0.6	16.8	668
8	Oldenburg	53° 15′	8° 15′	16.9	0.7	16.2	797
9	Bremerhaven	53° 30′	8° 30′	17.0	0.7	16.3	812
10	Hamburg	53° 30′	10° 00′	17.3	0.0	17.3	740
11	Wilhelmshaven	53° 30′	8° 15′	16.4	0.8	15.6	693
12	Lübeck	53° 45′	10° 45′	17.7	0.1	17.6	632
13	Schwerin	53° 45′	11° 30′	17.5	−0.1	17.6	627
14	Rostock	54° 00′	12° 15′	17.5	0.4	17.1	563

In many lines of geographical enquiry, the student meets, or, indeed, actively seeks, two sets of data which are linked by space or time. Fig. 63 quotes data for a selection of German (West and East) meteorological stations north of latitude 52°N. It offers a choice of paired variables. Latitude and longitude may each be linked in turn to data contained in columns 5 to 8. Is there, it might be asked, any relationship between longitude and mean annual range of temperature ? For investigations of this nature we have at hand the varied techniques of *correlation*.

Correlation

Scatter Diagrams (or Scatter Graphs)

This is the simplest and most visual of the available techniques. It is based on familiar horizontal (x) and vertical (y) axes. Each variable claims an axis which is scaled appropriately. By convention the horizontal axis serves the independent variable, and the vertical the dependent. Data is plotted against the scales on both axes. If the points fall on a straight line rising at an angle from left to right, as in Fig. 64, we recognise *perfect positive* correlation, for one variable

Fig. 64 *Perfect positive correlation (+1): one variable increases in proportion to the other*

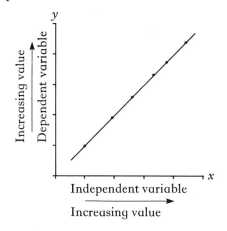

Fig. 65 *Perfect negative correlation (−1): one variable decreases as the other increases*

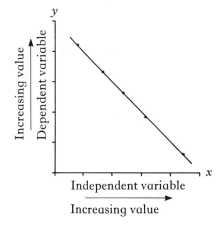

Fig. 66 *No correlation (0) between the variables: a random pattern is displayed*

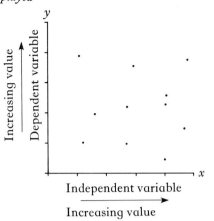

increases in proportion to the other. Fig. 65 illustrates another possibility. The plotted points again lie on a straight line, but in this case the slope is down to the right. This represents *perfect negative* correlation, for one variable decreases as the other increases. When there is no correlation between the variables, a random pattern such as that in Fig. 66 is displayed.

The precision of perfectly straight lines as seen in Figs. 64 and 65 is seldom encountered in reality. A more realistic example will be afforded by consideration of the data for longitude and mean annual range of temperature extracted from Fig. 63. Common sense enables us to distinguish dependent and independent variables. Temperatures may vary with longitude, but the reverse is clearly impossible. Thus, mean annual range of temperature is dependent and takes the vertical axis. The scatter diagram is seen in Fig. 67. By no means do all the points fall on a straight line.

Fig. 67 *A scatter diagram of longitude and mean annual range of temperature using the data from Fig. 63*

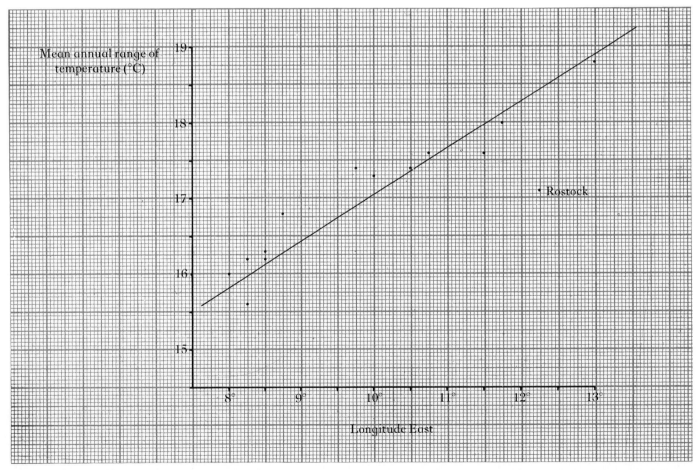

A scatter of points does, however, rise steadily from left to right, showing that in general terms, mean annual range of temperature increases with increasing distance east of Greenwich. Correlation is not perfect, but a degree of positive correlation between the two variables may be recognised. This may be emphasised by the insertion of a *best-fit line*. This is done subjectively by eye, and the aim is to achieve a balance of points on either side. A suggestion is seen in Fig. 67. If difficulty is experienced in choosing a path for the best-fit line, it is often helpful to calculate and plot the mean values of both sets of variables. The line should pass through this point.

The scatter diagram is simple to construct and gives a good visual impression of the relationship between paired data sets. Every point makes its contribution to the pattern. Not least amongst its advantages is that it highlights exceptional cases, known as *outliers* (perhaps Rostock in Fig. 67) which may be of particular significance or interest, and worthy of investigation. In general terms, the narrower the scatter of points, the stronger the correlation. A scatter diagram does not, however, provide an accurate measure of the degree of correlation between two variables. Comparisons between scatter diagrams of different pairs of variables must therefore be imprecise.

It must be stressed that relationships suggested by a scatter diagram, or indicated by other correlation techniques, are not necessarily *causal relationships*. We cannot conclude from Fig. 67 that longitude causes variations in mean annual range of temperature. If variable A increases proportionately to variable B, it does not follow that A is responsible for the rise in B, or B for A. There could well be a third variable that is responsible for both. However, if a significant statistical relationship is established, it prompts the geographer to seek explanation by whatever methods may be appropriate. Why, the geographer asks, does mean annual range of temperature in northern Germany vary with longitude?

---

1 Consider the data given in Fig. 63. Draw scatter diagrams to show the relationship between longitude east of Greenwich and:
  a mean annual precipitation;
  b mean January temperatures;
  c mean July temperatures.
In each case, insert a best-fit line, and ring any points which show marked deviation from the general trend.
Comment comparatively on the nature and relative strength of any correlations that may be suggested by your diagrams.

The best-fit line, as described above, is at best a rough and ready guide. With a scatter of points wider than that in Fig. 67, an appropriate path is hard to choose. Greater precision can, however, be achieved with the help of calculation, in which case the line of best-fit is termed a *regression line*.

The *semi-average* method is the most straightforward procedure for finding a regression line. The means of the two variables are calculated and plotted in the normal manner. Then the means of both sets of variables which lie respectively above and below the overall means are calculated. This has been done in Fig. 68. It will be appreciated that it is far easier to draw a line equidistant from three rather than from fourteen points.

The *least-squares* method is more precise but demands somewhat lengthy calculation. For each set of data the mean and the standard deviation are required. So, too, is the correlation coefficient (r), which is discussed in detail later (page 48). These are substituted in the formula:

$$y - \bar{y} = r . \frac{\sigma y}{\sigma x} (x - \bar{x})$$

where $\bar{y}$ = mean of variable y
  $\bar{x}$ = mean of variable x
  r = correlation coefficient
  σy = standard deviation of y
  σx = standard deviation of x

Solution for two selected values of x gives appropriate values of y, and plotting of these paired values gives points for the required regression line.

For illustration, again consider the data for longitude (x) and annual range of temperature (y) in Fig. 63. The relevant figures are quoted below.

$$\bar{x} = 9.98 \quad \sigma x = 1.61 \quad r = 0.896$$
$$\bar{y} = 17.02 \quad \sigma y = 0.85$$

y in terms of x is gained by substitution in the above formula:

$$y - \bar{y} = r . \frac{\sigma y}{\sigma x} (x - \bar{x})$$
$$y - 17.02 = 0.896 \frac{0.85}{1.61} (x - 9.98)$$
$$y - 17.02 = 0.47 (x - 9.98)$$
$$y - 17.02 = 0.47x - 4.69$$
$$y = 0.47x + 12.33$$

Two values of x are selected and substituted in turn. $x = 9$ and $x = 11$ are deemed convenient.

When $x = 9$: $y = 4.23 + 12.33 = 16.56$.
When $x = 11$: $y = 5.17 + 12.33 = 17.50$.
Thus, when $x = 9$, $y = 16.56$
  $x = 11, y = 17.50$.

These two pairs of values are plotted, and the line drawn through them is the required regression line.

Fig. 68 *Regression line found by semi-average method*

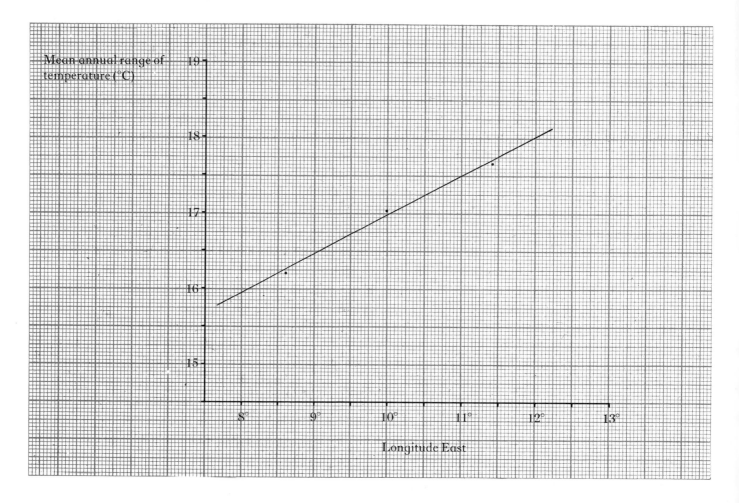

Mean annual range of temperature (°C)

Longitude East

Regression lines can be used to statistically predict, from a known independent value, the corresponding value of the dependent. When the regression line has been obtained by the least-squares method, this can be done mathematically. What, for instance, do we expect the annual range of temperature to be at 12°E ?

$$y = 0.47x + 12.33$$

When $x = 12$, $y = 5.64 + 12.33 = 17.97$, which, in °C, is the required figure.

Similarly, outliers, those exceptional cases so often worthy of close attention, may be mathematically measured. Take Rostock, for example. Its longitude is 12.25°:

$$y = 0.47x + 12.33$$

when $x = 12.25$, $y = 5.76 + 12.33 = 18.09$.

In fact, as Fig. 63 shows, the annual range of temperature in Rostock is 17.1°C which is virtually 1°C below what would be expected. Why, the geographer asks, should this be so ? Is there a factor other than longitude to be considered ? Is the fact that Rostock has a coastal location worthy of investigation ?

 Using **a.** the semi-average method and **b.** the least-squares method, draw regression lines to show the relationship between longitude east of Greenwich (Fig. 63) and
  i) mean annual precipitation;
  ii) mean January temperature;
  iii) mean July temperature.

Spearman Rank Correlation Coefficient

Fig. 67 (page 42) shows positive correlation between longitude and mean annual range of temperature, but fails to indicate, in more than general terms, the degree of correlation. This deficiency may be offset by calculation of the *Spearman rank correlation coefficient*, which will provide a reliable measure of the strength of the relationship between the two variables.

The first step in using Spearman rank is to formulate a *null hypothesis* (H_0). This is a conventional approach which makes for consistent interpretation of results in statistical tests. The wording of the null hypothesis is not guided by hard and fast rules, but it must state or imply the absence of any relationship, association or connection between the variables under consideration. For the present example, a suitable form of words would be "In northern Germany there is no significant relationship between longitude and mean annual range of temperature." Hopefully, calculation of the Spearman rank coefficient will enable us to reject this null hypothesis, and accept the alternative.

Spearman rank, as its name suggests, uses *ranked* data. Ranking, as indicated on page 6, requires care. If longitude values from Fig. 63 are written out as in Fig. 69, it is easy to check that values are truly listed from highest to lowest, and appropriate ranks may readily be awarded. Two or more identical values give *tied ranks*. For example, 8° 30′E occurs twice and commands tenth and eleventh places. The mean is taken and each is ranked 10.5. Similarly, 12.5 is the rank shared by the two stations on longitude 8° 15′E.

Data and ranks are tabled as in Fig. 70. For each station, the rank of the second variable is subtracted from that of the

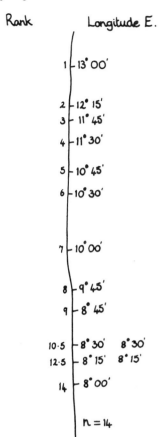

Fig. 69 *Ranking of longitude data*

Fig. 70 *Preparatory table for calculating values for Spearman rank coefficient*

Station no.	Long. E (to nearest 15′)	Rank order	Mean annual range of temp. (°C)	Rank order	d	d^2
1	8° 30′	10.5	16.2	11.5	−1	1
2	10° 30′	6	17.4	5.5	0.5	0.25
3	9° 45′	8	17.4	5.5	2.5	6.25
4	11° 45′	3	18.0	2	1	1
5	8° 00′	14	16.0	13	1	1
6	13° 00′	1	18.8	1	0	0
7	8° 45′	9	16.8	9	0	0
8	8° 15′	12.5	16.2	11.5	1	1
9	8° 30′	10.5	16.3	10	0.5	0.25
10	10° 00′	7	17.3	7	0	0
11	8° 15′	12.5	15.6	14	−1.5	2.25
12	10° 45′	5	17.6	3.5	1.5	2.25
13	11° 30′	4	17.6	3.5	0.5	0.25
14	12° 15′	2	17.1	8	−6	36

$$\Sigma d^2 = 51.5$$

first to give the difference in ranking (*d*). This is then squared to remove negative values and the answer is inserted in the column reserved for d^2. The values of d^2 are summed. The formula for the Spearman rank correlation coefficient is:

$$r_s = 1 - \frac{6\Sigma d^2}{n^3 - n}$$

where r_s = Spearman rank coefficient
 n = number of pairs of values
For the present example, substitution gives

$$r_s = 1 - \frac{309}{2730}$$
$$= 1 - 0.1132$$
$$= 0.887$$

The coefficient will always fall within a range that extends from $+1$ (perfect positive) to -1 (perfect negative). Zero, of course, indicates the absence of correlation. This range is presented visually in Fig. 71. The greater the value of r_s (positive *or* negative) the stronger the relationship between the two variables. An r_s of 0.750, for instance, represents a stronger correlation than, say, 0.600. Similarly, -0.700 indicates a more pronounced negative correlation than, say, -0.650, albeit only slightly so. The value achieved above, $r_s = 0.887$, may now be seen in perspective. It represents a strong degree of positive correlation.

When handling two or more sets of data, there is always the possibility that a result is due to chance. It is possible (though unlikely), for instance, that had 14 pairs of values been produced by guesswork, calculation could have yielded a coefficient of 0.887. In statistical terms a result is only truly *significant* when it can be demonstrated that it could

not have occurred by chance. Results, therefore, must always be tested for significance, that is, the probability of chance having influenced the result must be calculated. We must know the level of confidence that we may have in a result. Fig. 72 is a graph which enables us to test r_s for significance. The scale to the left accommodates the coefficient produced by calculation. The horizontal axis is scaled in *degrees of freedom*. This is obtained by subtracting 2 from the number of pairs of items in the data under investigation ($n - 2$). Note that the spacing on the horizontal axis is not even. It is an example of a logarithmic scale, which is considered on page 57. The curves on the graph represent the critical values for the quoted significance levels. A significance level of 0.1% means that the likelihood that the correlation occurred by chance is less than 1 in 1000. Similarly, 1% means 1 in 100, and at the 5% significance level, the likelihood of chance is 5 times in 100. The 5% significance level is known as the *rejection level*, for this is the level that must be achieved before the null hypothesis can be rejected.

The use of Fig. 72 may be illustrated with the aid of hypothetical examples. Assume that calculations based on 22 pairs of values gives $r_s = 0.5$. With 22 pairs, the number of degrees of freedom is $22 - 2 = 20$. Reference to the graph reveals that with 20 degrees of freedom, 0.5 is higher than the curve of the 5% significance level. We have sufficient confidence (95%) to reject the null hypothesis and accept the alternative. Suppose, for the sake of further illustration, that our hypothesis test had, in fact, yielded $r_s = 0.6$. This, as the graph indicates, is significant at the 1% level, giving us 99% confidence in the result. Similarly, with $r_s = 0.7$ the likelihood that correlation is due to chance is less than 1 in 1000, giving appropriately increased confidence. In contrast, let us assume $r_s = 0.4$ with 20 degrees of freedom. This coefficient fails to achieve the 5% significance level. The likelihood of chance is too great. The null hypothesis must be accepted, and it is concluded that there is no significant correlation between the variables.

Let us now return to our original worked example where, with $n = 14$, $r_s = 0.887$. By reference to Fig. 72 it is clear that this coefficient, with 12 degrees of freedom, is significant at the 0.1% level. We have ample confidence to reject the null hypothesis and to accept the alternative. We state, with 99.9% confidence, that, in northern Germany, there is significant correlation between longitude and mean annual range of temperature.

Although the Spearman rank coefficient depends on ranks rather than actual data, it is a most effective test of correlation, and its popularity is enhanced by the fact that the burden of calculation is relatively modest.

Finally, it is worth emphasising that significant correlations revealed by the Spearman test are statistical and not causal. Spearman rank does not provide explanations. Its great value is that it serves as a signpost pointing along

Fig. 71 *Range of* r_s *values*

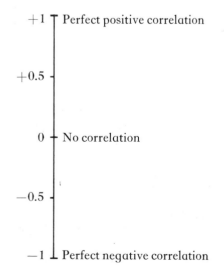

+1 ⊤ Perfect positive correlation

+0.5 ┤

0 ┼ No correlation

−0.5 ┤

−1 ⊥ Perfect negative correlation

Fig. 72 *Significance levels of the Spearman rank coefficient (r_s)*

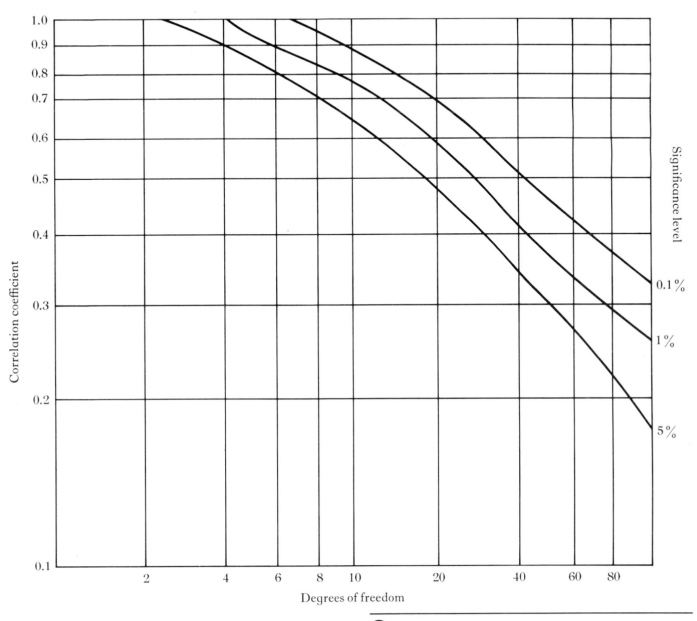

what may prove to be a productive avenue of research. Moreover, when the null hypothesis cannot be rejected, it is not a case of time wasted. It usually means that a fruitless journey down an academic cul-de-sac has been avoided.

 Using the data in Fig. 63, calculate the Spearman rank correlation coefficient to obtain a measure of the degree of correlation between longitude east of Greenwich and

a mean annual precipitation;
b mean January temperature;
c mean July temperature.

In each case, assess the statistical significance of your answer.

Product-moment Correlation Coefficient

This somewhat clumsy title introduces a powerful and precise testing of correlation. It is illustrated by a worked example using the variables previously tested by Spearman rank (page 45). The same null hypothesis is appropriate.

Fig. 73 is a layout convenient for recording the necessary calculations. The variables, labelled x and y, are recorded in columns A and B. The values in each column are summed and divided by n (in this example, 14) to give the mean, that is, $\bar{x}$ and $\bar{y}$. For column C, $\bar{x}$ is subtracted from x, and the answer is squared for column D. The results of similar calculations using variable y are recorded in columns E and F. The final column receives the product of columns C and E, that is $(x - \bar{x})(y - \bar{y})$. Columns D, F and G are summed.

The formula for the product-moment correlation coefficient (r) is:

$$r = \frac{\Sigma(x - \bar{x})(y - \bar{y})}{\sqrt{[\Sigma(x - \bar{x})^2][\Sigma(y - \bar{y})^2]}}$$

This may appear to be a rather formidable formula, but all the required figures appear at the foot of the columns G, D and F respectively. For this example, substitution gives

$$r = \frac{17.2}{\sqrt{36.41 \times 10.15}}$$

$$= \frac{17.2}{\sqrt{369.56}}$$

$$= \frac{17.2}{19.22}$$

$$= 0.895$$

This answer, tested with Fig. 72, is seen to be significant at the 0.1 % level. The null hypothesis can be rejected.

An alternative formula for the product-moment correlation coefficient is:

$$r = \frac{\dfrac{\Sigma(x - \bar{x})(y - \bar{y})}{n}}{\sigma x . \sigma y}$$

where σx = standard deviation of variable x

σy = standard deviation of variable y

If the values of σ are available—and they may be gained in a moment by using one of many calculators of relatively modest cost which provide this function—this formula may prove to be a less tedious route to the required coefficient.

The product-moment correlation coefficient, making use of actual data rather than ranks, is more accurate than Spearman rank, but the difference is slight, and must be paid for in greater complexity of calculation.

Fig. 73 *Preparatory table for calculating the product-moment correlation coefficient*

	A	B	C	D	E	F	G
	Long. °E	Mean annual range of temp. (°C)					
	x	y	$x - \bar{x}$	$(x - \bar{x})^2$	$y - \bar{y}$	$(y - \bar{y})^2$	$(x - \bar{x})(y - \bar{y})$
1	8.50	16.2	−1.48	2.19	−0.82	0.67	1.21
2	10.50	17.4	0.52	0.27	0.38	0.14	0.20
3	9.75	17.4	−0.23	0.05	0.38	0.14	−0.09
4	11.75	18.0	1.77	3.13	0.98	0.96	1.74
5	8.00	16.0	−1.98	3.92	−1.02	1.04	2.02
6	13.00	18.8	3.02	9.12	1.78	3.17	5.38
7	8.75	16.8	−1.23	1.51	−0.22	0.05	0.27
8	8.25	16.2	−1.73	2.99	−0.82	0.67	1.42
9	8.50	16.3	−1.48	2.19	−0.72	0.52	1.07
10	10.00	17.3	0.02	0.00	0.28	0.08	0.01
11	8.25	15.6	−1.73	2.99	−1.42	2.02	2.46
12	10.75	17.6	0.77	0.59	0.58	0.34	0.45
13	11.50	17.6	1.52	2.31	0.58	0.34	0.88
14	12.25	17.1	2.27	5.15	0.08	0.01	0.18
Σ	139.75	238.3		36.41		10.15	17.20

$$\bar{x} = 9.98 \qquad \bar{y} = 17.02$$

4 Using the data in Fig. 63, calculate the product-moment correlation coefficient to obtain a measure of the degree of correlation between longitude and
a mean annual precipitation;
b mean January temperatures;
c mean July temperatures.
In each case, assess the statistical significance of the coefficient you have calculated.

Fig. 74 *Hypothetical distribution of farms*

Area A	Area B	Area C
25%	50%	25%
21 farms	59 farms	20 farms

The Chi-squared Test

This is a useful statistical technique of wide application. Chi is the Greek letter pronounced ky, and chi-squared is symbolically written χ^2. A hypothetical example will illustrate how it is used.

Fig. 74 represents an expanse of farmland consisting, in the proportions indicated, of three contrasting rock types. The land supports a total of 100 farms. It is observed that there are 21 in area A, 59 in B, and 20 in C. Now, if mere chance were the only factor that influenced the distribution of farms, it would be reasonable to expect that area A, with 25% of the area, would have 25% of the farms. The same would be true of area C. Area B, with 50% of the area, would be expected to hold 50% of the farms. Thus, we have two sets of values—those observed in reality and those that could be expected. They may readily be compared if tabled as in Fig. 75. Area B is seen to claim more than that which may be described as its fair share, and A and C suffer in comparison. On this evidence it is tempting to jump to the conclusion that there is a relationship between the two distributions, and to assume that rock type influences the location of farms. But look again at the figures. The differences between observed and expected values are by no means dramatic. They could merely be the result of random variation. Chi-squared will indicate whether or not the differences are statistically significant.

A null hypothesis is the starting-point. In this example, "There is no significant association between rock type and the distribution of farms", is one possible form. The formula for chi-squared is:

$$\chi^2 = \Sigma \frac{(O - E)^2}{E}$$

Solution is simplified if Fig. 75 is expanded into Fig. 76 where the additional rows guide us step by step through the necessary calculations to a result of $\chi^2 = 3.26$.

The result of these calculations is not, of course, an end in itself—it must be interpreted. χ^2 is a measure of the divergence of values observed and expected. If they are identical,

Fig. 75 *Comparison of the number of farms observed (O) and the number expected (E).*

	A	B	C	Total
Observed (O)	21	59	20	100
Expected (E)	25	50	25	100

Fig. 76 *Table for calculation of Chi-squared (χ^2)*

	A	B	C
Observed (O)	21	59	20
Expected (E)	25	50	25
O − E	−4	9	−5
(O−E)²	16	81	25
$\frac{(O-E)^2}{E}$	0.64	1.62	1.0

$$\Sigma \frac{(O - E)^2}{E} \qquad 0.64 + 1.62 + 1.0 = 3.26 = \chi^2$$

then $\chi^2 = 0$. When χ^2 is small, it is likely that the divergence is due to chance. The larger the value of χ^2, the greater the likelihood that factors other than chance have exerted an influence.

Chi-squared is tested for significance against the critical values given in Fig. 77. Note that values are quoted against *degrees of freedom*. When there is only one set of observed values, the number of degrees of freedom is found by simply subtracting 1 from the number of observations in the set. In the above example with one observation (frequency of farms) for each of three areas, there are $3 - 1 = 2$ degrees of freedom. Had there been four areas, there would have

Fig. 77 *Table of critical values of χ^2*

Degrees of freedom	Levels of probability		
	5% (0.05)	1% (0.01)	0.1% (0.001)
1	3.84	6.64	10.83
2	5.99	9.21	13.82
3	7.82	11.35	16.27
4	9.49	13.28	18.47
5	11.07	15.09	20.52
6	12.59	16.81	22.46
7	14.07	18.48	24.32
8	15.51	20.09	26.13
9	16.92	21.67	27.88
10	18.31	23.21	29.59

been three degrees of freedom. The other columns in Fig. 77 indicate levels of probability (p). When $p = 5\%$ (or 0.05), it means that 5 times in 100 a result could be due to chance. With $p = 1\%$ and 0.1%, the role of chance is reduced to 1 in 100 and 1 in 1000 respectively. The critical values listed in the table must be equalled or exceeded to achieve the stated level of probability. The 5% probability (significance) level is the lowest that is generally acceptable. The others are preferred, for they inspire greater confidence in the result of an investigation.

Testing the example worked above will provide illustration. The table reveals that, for two degrees of freedom, $\chi^2 = 3.26$ is below the critical value of 5%. More than 5 times in 100 the differences between O and E could be due to chance. This is too great an uncertainty. Our confidence in the result is inadequate. The null hypothesis must be accepted. We conclude, therefore, that there is no connection between rock type and farm distribution.

Pause for practice. Assume that in the area under investigation (Fig. 74) there are, in fact, 19 farms in A, 63 in B and 18 in C. The expected values do not change. The null hypothesis remains the same. Apply the chi-squared test to these observations.

Hopefully, your answer is 6.78. Test this against the values for 2 degrees of freedom (Fig. 77). It exceeds the critical value of the 5% probability level. The likelihood that the differences between O and E are due to chance is less than 5 in 100. This gives us the confidence to reject the null hypothesis. It can be concluded that, at the 95% confidence level, the distribution of farms has been influenced by rock type, and search may begin for an explanation.

Further points are worthy of note. The chi-squared test can only be used with frequency data. If the information available is the result of measurement, it must first be

grouped into classes. Measurements of pebble size, for instance, could be classed as: <20 mm; between 20 and 40 mm; and >40 mm. The number of observations must be greater than 20, and, for preference, at least twice as great. Also, the number of values both observed and expected should be greater than 5.

 Investigation into the possible influence of rock type on village location in part of the English lowlands produced the data tabled below:

	Clay	Greensand	Chalk	Total
% of area	50	30	20	100
No. of villages	29	31	10	70

Apply the chi-squared test and, with the aid of Fig. 77, give a full interpretation of the result.

 A deposit of boulder clay was sampled and the orientation of 80 rock fragments was measured. Data was classed as follows:

Orientation	0–44°	45°–89°	90°–134°	135°–179°
Frequency	12	19	35	14

Formulate an appropriate null hypothesis, apply the chi-squared test and interpret the result.

A slightly more elaborate application of chi-squared may now be examined. Suppose that the topic of investigation is the possible relationship between type of agriculture and type of rock. Research produces the data tabled in Fig. 78. At first glance, it appears that rock C favours arable agriculture, whereas, on soils derived from other rocks, dairying has the edge. But is this a safe assumption? Has pure chance had a role to play? The data must be tested for significance, and the chi-squared test is an appropriate technique.

The first step is again the formulation of a null hypothesis (H_0). "Type of farming does not differ significantly with rock type", is one suggestion. "Differences in type of farming are not associated with differences in rock type", is another possibility.

Application of the chi-squared test is eased if the data is set in a contingency table of two rows and three columns, as seen in Fig. 79a. Check the totals of columns and rows, and check that the sum of these totals equals the grand total that appears in the bottom right-hand corner.

The triangular spaces are reserved for expected values which are obtained by calculation. For each cell, multiply the column total by the row total and divide by the grand total. For the top left cell, for example, the expected value is $\frac{22 \times 57}{103} = 12.17$.

Fig. 78 *Data of type of agriculture and rock type*

Rock type / Farming type	A	B	C
Arable	9	8	40
Dairy	13	15	18

Fig. 79a *Contingency table for χ^2. The triangular spaces are for expected values obtained by calculation.*

Rock type / Farming type	A	B	C	Total
Arable	9	8	40	57
Dairying	13	15	18	46
Total	22	23	58	103

Fig. 79b *The completed contingency table*

Rock type / Farming type	A	B	C	Total
Arable	9 / 12.17	8 / 12.73	40 / 32.10	57
Dairying	13 / 9.83	15 / 10.27	18 / 25.90	46
Total	22	23	58	103

$$\chi^2 = \Sigma \left\{ \begin{array}{ccc} 0.83 & 1.76 & 1.94 \\ 1.02 & 2.18 & 2.41 \end{array} \right\} = 10.14$$

This, and the expected values calculated for other cells, are recorded in Fig. 79b. It is wise to check that the expected values add up to the sum of the observed values in both column and row. Note that statistically speaking, it is perfectly possible to have a value of 12.17 farms. The formula

$$\frac{(O - E)^2}{E}$$

is solved for each cell, and results are neatly recorded beneath the table (Fig. 79b). χ^2 is the sum of the six cell values. In this example it is 10.14.

Before this statistic can be tested for significance, the number of degrees of freedom must be determined. When, as here, there is more than one set of observed values, this is done by multiplying the (number of columns — 1) by (the number of rows — 1). In this case it is $(3 - 1)(2 - 1) = 2 \times 1 = 2$ degrees of freedom. Tested against Fig. 77, it is seen that $\chi^2 = 10.14$ with two degrees of freedom is significant at the 1% level. The possibility that data differences are due to chance is less than 1 in 100. We can, therefore, be 99% confident that differences are *not* due to chance. The null hypothesis can be rejected at the 99% confidence level. It can be stated, with 99% confidence, that in the area under investigation, there is a significant relationship between type of farming and type of rock. It is important to stress that this result does not prove that agriculture is determined solely by rock type. Other possible variations— relief, for instance, need to be considered. However, chi-squared has opened the door to a profitable line of enquiry in the search for explanation.

Finally, it is worthy of note that the contingency table may be composed of any number of columns and rows. The greater the number, however, the greater the likelihood that one or more cells fails to achieve the minimum value of 5. Should this happen, it is usually possible to combine one or more observations or classes so as to exceed the critical figure.

7 In 1965, in the Cheddar region, there were 58 farms making cheese on a commercial scale. After a decade of decline, only 22 survived. It was suggested that the size of the cheese-making enterprise was a factor influencing survival. Farms were classed as large or small depending on whether the throughput of milk was more or less than the median value. Data was tabled as seen below.

	Survivors	Non-survivors
Large	16	14
Small	6	22

Formulate a null hypothesis, apply the chi-squared test and interpret your result.

8 As part of an investigation into motorway accidents in Greater Manchester, it was hypothesised that weather conditions were an important factor. Research revealed that in wet weather the M61, M62 and M63 experienced 32, 272 and 96 accidents respectively. In dry weather, the figures were 32, 218 and 30.

Formulate a null hypothesis, apply the chi-squared test and interpret your results.

Consolidation

9 The table gives a variety of data for a random sample of countries. Use:

a scatter diagrams,
b Spearman rank,
c product-moment,

to test for possible statistical correlations between the percentage of working population engaged in agriculture and:

   i) birth rate;
   ii) energy consumption;
   iii) population density;
   iv) mean life expectancy;
   v) population per hospital bed.

In each case, evaluate the nature, strength and significance of your answer.

	Country	% of working population in agriculture	Birth rate (per thousand)	Energy consumption (kg of coal equivalent per capita)	Population density (per km²)	Mean life expectancy at birth (yr)	Population per hospital bed
1	Austria	10	11	4013	89	72	88
2	Britain	2	12	5268	228	71	117
3	Cameroon	82	42	98	17	41	390
4	E. Germany	10	14	6789	155	71	93
5	Guyana	23	28	1072	4	61	199
6	Iraq	42	47	725	28	53	491
7	Japan	13	16	3679	309	75	95
8	Laos	75	45	61	15	40	401
9	Lebanon	12	35	533	301	63	260
10	Rwanda	90	51	17	173	41	510
11	Saudi Arabia	61	50	1901	4	45	840
12	Sri Lanka	54	30	106	217	66	334
13	Upper Volta	83	48	18	24	32	1174
14	Uruguay	13	21	1000	16	68	235
15	Yugoslavia	40	17	2016	86	68	167
16	Zambia	68	50	548	8	44	250

10 Consider the data presented in the table below.

a Draw a scatter diagram of mean July temperatures against latitude. Insert a best-fit line. Identify any stations which deviate considerably from the best-fit line, and suggest possible explanations.

b Use *either* Spearman rank *or* product-moment to calculate the correlation coefficient. Comment fully on the strength and significance of the relationship between latitude and mean July temperatures.

c Repeat exercises **a** and **b** using data for latitude and mean January temperatures.

d Using experience gained above, comment critically on the relative merits of the techniques employed.

	Station	Latitude N (to nearest 10′)	Mean July Temps. °C	Mean Jan. Temps. °C
1	Kelso	55° 40′	14.9	2.3
2	Belper	53° 00′	16.2	3.1
3	Penzance	50° 10′	16.4	7.2
4	Braemar	57° 00′	13.1	0.6
5	Birmingham	52° 30′	16.2	3.5
6	Stornoway	58° 10′	13.3	4.3
7	Felixstowe	52° 00′	17.2	3.9
8	Lerwick	60° 10′	12.0	3.1
9	Keswick	54° 40′	15.2	3.7
10	Ft. Augustus	57° 10′	14.3	2.6
11	Margate	51° 20′	17.4	4.6
12	Cromer	52° 00′	16.4	3.7
13	Aberdeen	57° 10′	14.0	2.4
14	Wick	58° 30′	12.9	3.4
15	Tenby	51° 40′	15.9	5.5
16	Buxton	53° 20′	14.3	1.9
17	Tiree	56° 30′	13.7	5.3
18	Durham	54° 50′	15.3	2·8
19	Weymouth	50° 30′	16.8	5.6
20	Valley	53° 20′	15.1	5.6
21	North Berwick	56° 00′	14.8	3.3
22	Greenock	55° 50′	15.1	3.8

11 A student investigating the possible relationship between altitude and vegetation sampled a Pennine hillside with the following results:

Species \ Altitude	< 200 m	200 – 400 m	> 400 m
Tufted Hairgrass	9	11	28
Common Bent	16	15	14

Formulate a null hypothesis, apply the chi-squared test and interpret your result.

12 Describe fully how, using the information contained in Fig. 128, page 90, you would test the hypothesis that there is a significant association between altitude and farm location.

Section D · Graphs and Diagrams

Fig. 80 *Landings of fish of British taking*

	Landed weight (thousand tonnes)									
	1970	1971	1972	1973	1974	1975	1976	1977	1978	1979
Total all fish	963	964	942	998	955	855	917	904	945	827
Total wet fish	910	913	888	932	894	792	839	830	881	764
Total shellfish	53	51	54	66	61	63	78	74	64	63
Demersal Species										
Total	727	711	669	658	637	575	569	494	429	363
Cod	344	305	301	273	267	242	211	147	125	108
Haddock	176	181	157	149	126	113	128	123	82	73
Plaice	44	44	40	38	29	28	32	36	32	32
Saithe (coalfish)	50	53	47	56	44	35	40	35	31	19
Whiting	30	39	36	34	38	44	46	47	55	58
Other demersal	83	89	88	108	133	113	112	106	104	73
Pelagic Species										
Total	183	202	219	274	257	217	270	336	452	401
Herring	141	143	146	151	141	107	85	40	15	3
Mackerel	5	6	9	21	30	48	87	187	321	353
Other pelagic	37	53	64	102	86	62	98	109	116	45

Extracted from Annual Abstract of Statistics (HMSO)

Fig. 80 is a table of statistics relating to the British fishing industry. It is not the most riveting piece of literature, but it has its stories to tell. For the years concerned it records the decline in total landings and the fluctuating fortunes of individual species. The stories accurately told by dull statistics may be brightly illuminated if presented in a visual manner. For this we can choose from a variety of graphs and diagrams. These add nothing to our store of information, but portray it with clarity and impact.

Lines

The *linear* graph is, perhaps, the simplest, most familiar type of graph in common use. It is successfully used to illustrate variations with time, or, less frequently, with distance. Fig. 81 is an example based on the table of fishing statistics. It plots the landings of cod from 1970 to 1979.

The two variables have an axis each. The horizontal, as is customary, supports the independent variable, in this case, time. The dependent variable, landings, is scaled on the vertical, which is often duplicated to make the graph easier to read. Both scales should be chosen with care, for they affect the size and proportions of the finished graph. There are no rules for this; it is a matter of judgement and taste. As with all graphs, aim for dimensions that balance size with clarity. Seek pleasing proportions and avoid the temptation to fill the page. If one axis is excessively longer than the other, the graph presents an unbalanced picture. The vertical scale should extend to just beyond the highest value from a starting-point of zero.

If, when values are high, economy of space suggests that the scale should start higher than zero, the point should be emphasised by the convention illustrated in Fig. 82.

Values are plotted by neat dots or tiny crosses. Dots are joined by straight lines except when change can be assumed to be continuous, in which case smooth curves are preferred.

53

Fig. 81 *A linear graph plotting the landings of cod from 1970 to 1979*

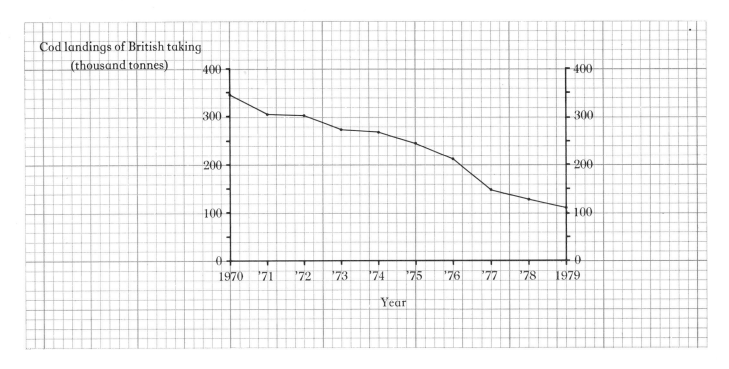

Fig. 82 *Scales starting higher than zero should be indicated by a partly zigzag axis*

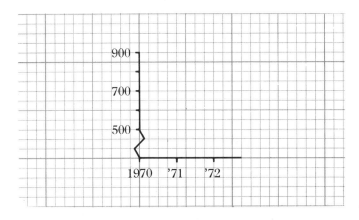

In drawing any graph, precision and neatness are skills to practise. The former is achieved by patient plotting and a fine-pointed pencil. Neatness is the key to attractive appearance. Avoid clutter. It is, for instance, seldom necessary to number every division on the vertical scale. Take care with letters and labels. Ensure that all the necessary information is included for full interpretation.

One pair of axes may support more than a single variable. This is illustrated by Fig. 83, which shows the varying contribution of demersal and pelagic species to total wet fish landings. In a multiple graph of this nature, there are points to note. The vertical scale must be appropriate to all the dependent variables, the number of which must not be excessive if confusion is to be avoided. The lines on the graph should be clearly distinguished. Colour is an obvious asset. The lines may be labelled, or keyed beside the graph.

Fig. 84 illustrates an effective variety of linear graph. It is based on the data for pelagic species (Fig. 80). The variables are plotted in sequence. The first (lowest) is drawn with values for 'other pelagic species' as read from the table. Points for the second line of the graph are obtained by summing the values of two variables (other pelagic and mackerel). The sum of all three values gives the final line, which, in this simple example, equals the total pelagic landings. Spaces between the lines are neatly shaded, and labelled or keyed. In this compound linear graph, variations through time are represented by area. Visual impact is therefore greater, but a pair of dividers are needed to read off the sectional values.

Fig. 83 *A multiple linear graph showing the contribution of demersal and pelagic species to total landings between 1970 and 1979*

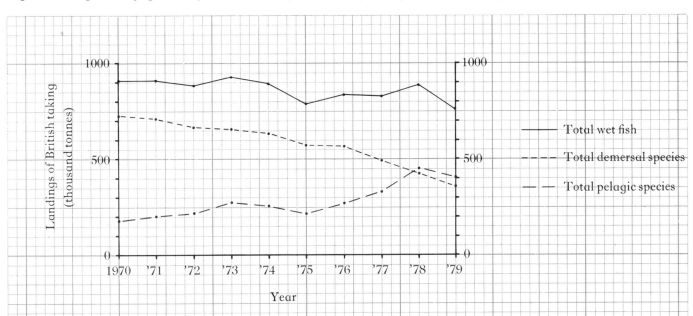

Fig. 84 *A compound linear graph of the landings of pelagic fish from 1970 to 1979*

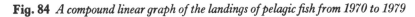

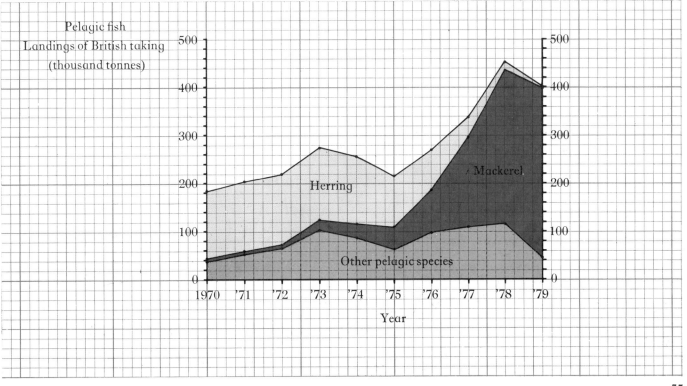

Fig. 85 *Coffee production in Brazil*

Coffee Production (thousand tonnes)	1967	1968	1969	1970	1971	1972	1973	1974	1975	1976	1977	1978	1979	1980	1981
Brazil	1398	990	1284	755	1795	1510	873	1650	1228	400	958	1226	1295	998	1878
World	4268	3749	4348	3985	5195	4903	4103	4893	4430	3653	4323	4608	4972	4694	5808

Fig. 86 *A linear graph of coffee production in Brazil from 1967 to 1981. The running mean enables trends to be more easily identified.*

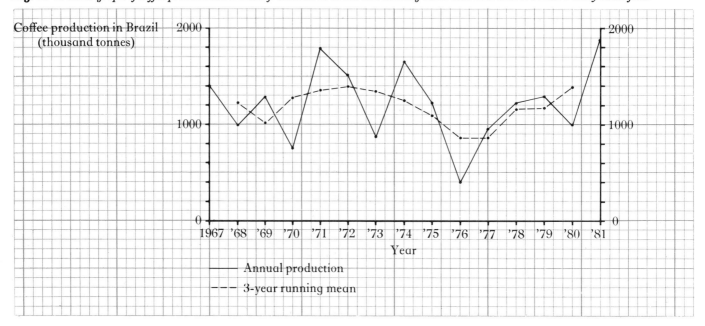

Fig. 87 *A linear graph of coffee production in Brazil from 1967 to 1981 showing the variation above and below mean production*

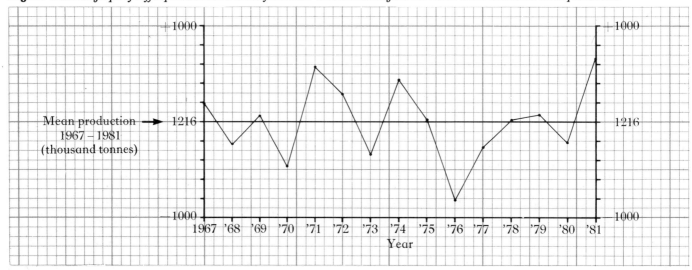

In the examples given above, change through time is relatively steady. This is not always the case. When variables fluctuate widely from year to year, the linear graph may zigzag sharply. Coffee production in Brazil provides illustration. Statistics are given in Fig. 85 and the graph is seen in Fig. 86. The curve is smoother and trends become easier to identify if, instead of annual totals, a *running mean* is plotted. The dashed curve in Fig. 86 shows a three-year running mean. The value plotted for 1968 is the mean of production in 1967, 1968, and 1969. Similarly 1969 is derived from the figures for 1968, 1969, and 1970.

Fig. 87 illustrates another way in which the fluctuating fortunes of the Brazilian coffee growers can be illustrated. The mean is calculated for the full span of years, and is clearly indicated. The mean is subtracted from each year's production and plotted as a plus or minus value. Alternatively, variations may be graphed as percentages.

---

1 Using data from Fig. 80, draw:
  a linear graphs to illustrate annual landings, from 1970 to 1979, of i) haddock, ii) plaice, iii) mackerel;
  b a compound linear graph to illustrate the varying contribution of cod, haddock, plaice, saithe and other species to total landings of demersal species from 1970 to 1979.

2 Using data from Fig. 85, draw linear graphs to illustrate:
  a world coffee production 1967 to 1981;
  b the three-year running mean;
  c variation above and below mean world production.

All the above graphs carry familiar arithmetical scales. In Fig. 88, however, we see the distinctive pattern of *semi-logarithmic* or '*log normal*' ruling. Examine it closely. It is the horizontal axis that is normal, for it bears equal divisions. The vertical has a logarithmic scale. Fig. 89 is a reminder that the difference between the logarithms of successive numbers becomes progressively smaller. This is reflected in the scale, for in cycles of 10, horizontal rulings become progressively closer. On printed sheets, the major divisions are subdivided into 10 or 5 according to the space available, to facilitate the plotting of intermediate values. The scale is numbered in relation to the data that is to be graphed. An indication of the varied possibilities is given in Fig. 88. Note that the cycles rise in multiples of 10, and that no home can be found for zero. The number of cycles required will depend on the range of the data.

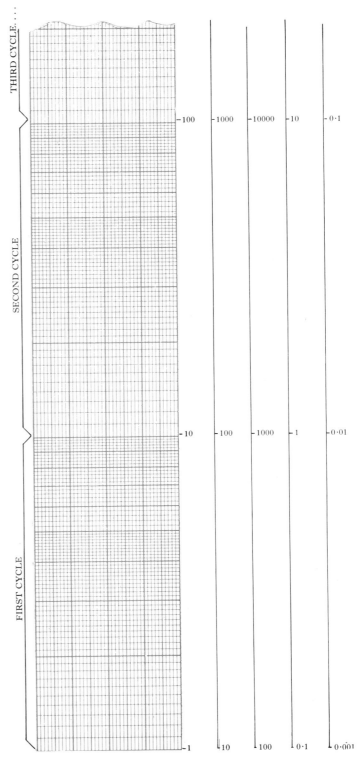

Fig. 88 *Semi-logarithmic or log normal ruling with examples of how the vertical scale can be labelled*

Fig. 89 *The difference between logarithms of successive numbers becomes progressively smaller*

No.	Log	No.	Log
1	0.0000	6	0.7782
2	0.3010	7	0.8451
3	0.4771	8	0.9031
4	0.6021	9	0.9542
5	0.6990	10	1.0000

Fig. 90 *The populations of four settlements at 10-yearly intervals. The growth rates are plotted in Fig. 91.*

					thousands
	1900	**1910**	**1920**	**1930**	**1940**
A	60	90	135	202.5	303.8
B	12	18	27	40.5	60.8
C	50	55	60.5	66.6	133.1
D	20	30	40	50	60

	1950	**1960**	**1970**	**1980**
A	455.6	683.4	1025.2	1537.5
B	91.1	136.7	205	307.5
C	266.2	532.4	1064.8	2129.6
D	70	80	90	100

A semi-logarithmic graph is of particular value when the *rate* of change (increase or decrease) is of greater interest than the amount of change. A straight line on the graph indicates a steady rate of change. The steeper the slope, the greater the rate. Population study is but one field in which the semi-logarithmic graph proves its worth; and information given in Fig. 90 serves for illustration. A, B, C and D represent four hypothetical settlements, and the figures represent their populations at ten-yearly intervals. A quick comparison of the figures for settlements A and B may well give the impression that the rate of growth is higher for A than for B. However, when the figures are plotted on semi-logarithmic graph paper (Fig. 91), curves A and B are straight and parallel, indicating that they share the same constant rate of increase, which is, in fact, 50% per decade. The curve for settlement C reveals a constant but relatively low rate of increase for the first three decades, but then the rate increases dramatically. The case of D is included for

Fig. 91 *Comparison of the population growth rates of settlements A, B, C and D* ▶

58

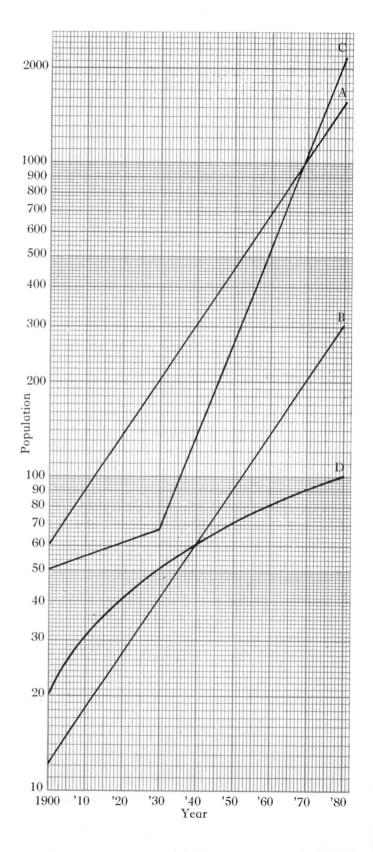

comparison. Each decade its population increases by a regular amount, but not at a regular rate, and the plot on the graph produces a curve. A further advantage of semi-logarithmic graph paper is that, because of the compression of the vertical scale, it can happily accommodate data of wide range.

Graph paper bearing logarithmic scales on both axes is available for specialist requirements. Understandably, it is known as 'log log' graph paper.

3 Plot the data contained in Fig. 90 on normal graph paper and compare your graph with Fig. 91. Comment on the contrasts observed.

4 Obtain, for a convenient span of years, the population figures for two local towns. Plot on semi-logarithmic graph paper, and comment on any similarities or differences in rate of growth that may be revealed.

Bars

The bar, or column, is an effective and versatile device for the visual representation of statistics. An example is given in Fig. 92. Familiar axes form the framework. The vertical rises from zero, and is neatly and appropriately scaled. The bars rise up to relevant levels from spaces on the horizontal axis. In construction, the use of graph paper will ensure that the bars have parallel sides and level summits. Clarity is improved if space is left between the bars, and here, also, graph paper is a practical asset. As with all graphs, size and proportion are important and the width of bar must be carefully chosen. The finished graph is made clearer if the bars are lightly shaded in a single colour.

Fig. 92 *A bar graph to illustrate cod landings from 1970 to 1979*

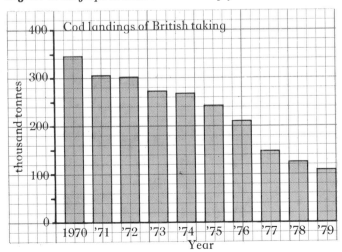

Fig. 93 *Compound bar graph of landings of pelagic fish from 1970 to 1979*

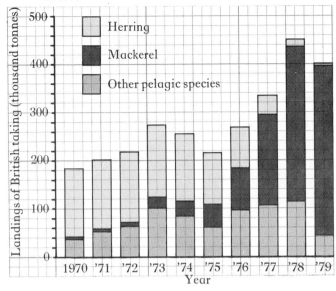

Fig. 94 *Bar graph to compare the landings of demersal species in 1970 with 1979 landings*

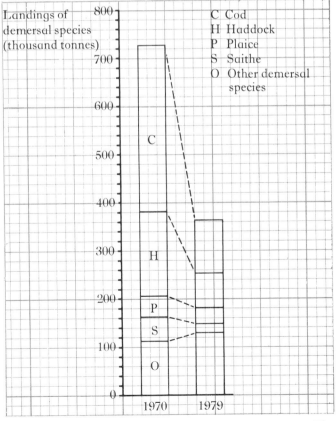

Fig. 95 *Bar graph to compare the land use of two Teesdale parishes, Westwick and Gilmonby*

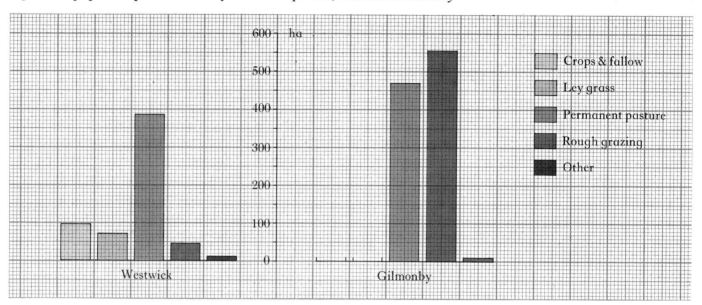

Fig. 96 *Two further examples of bar graphs:*

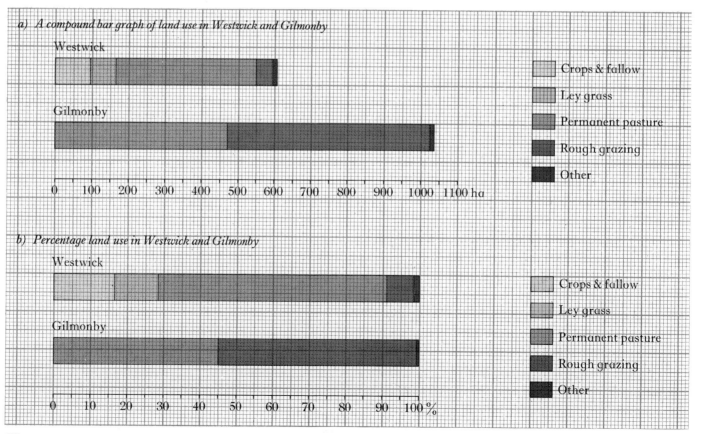

Fig. 97 *A bar graph of coffee production in Brazil from 1967 to 1981, showing the variation above and below mean production.*

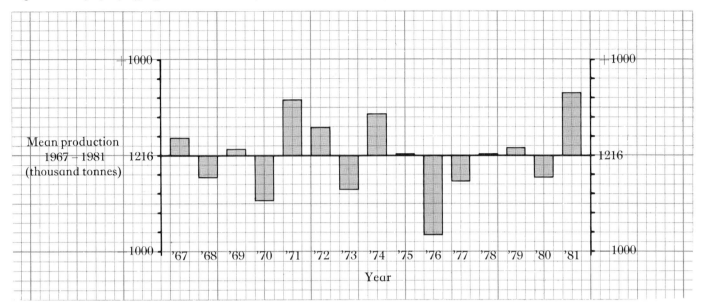

Bar graphs, like linear graphs, may be compounded to illustrate subdivisions of a total value. Fig. 93 treats landings of pelagic species in this way. Critically compare this graph with Fig. 84 and decide which is the more effective.

The following examples give a hint of the great versatility of the useful bar. Fig. 94 is drawn for demersal species and emphasises change over the period in question. The dotted links between the bars are an optional extra designed to aid interpretation. The bar is not restricted to data that varies with time. It is commonly used to show contrasts between places or areas. This is the case with Fig. 95, which shows full land use in a pair of Teesdale parishes. Variation on a theme is seen in Fig. 96a. It is a reminder that bars need not stand vertically. Fig. 96b shows percentages, and the bars, therefore, are of equal length. Fig. 97 is a treatment of Brazilian coffee production which stands comparison with Fig. 87.

 5 Using data from Fig. 80, draw:
   a a bar graph to illustrate landings of herring from 1970 to 1979;
   b a bar graph to illustrate the varying contribution of cod, haddock, plaice, saithe and other species, to the total landings of demersal species from 1970 to 1979;
   c a pair of compound bars to illustrate the contrasts in landings of pelagic species in 1970 and 1979.

 6 Using data for world coffee production (Fig. 85), draw:
   a a simple bar graph to illustrate annual coffee production from 1967 to 1981;
   b a bar graph to show the variation of production about the mean for the period.

Circles

Circles, like bars, are popular vehicles for the representation of statistics. Examine Fig. 98. The area of each circle is proportional to the landings of herring in the year indicated, and the trend of decline is mirrored in the shrinking size of the circles. Dimensions are derived from πr^2, the familiar formula for the area of a circle. π is a constant, and so area is proportional to the square root of the value.

When several circles are required, it is useful to compile a simple table such as the one in Fig. 99. The second column contains values taken from the herring statistics in Fig. 80. A calculator equipped with a $\sqrt{}$ key, speeds the completion of the third column. These figures, if treated as millimetres and used as radii, will give a set of circles proportional in area to the original values. But in this example, as is often the case, dimensions are excessive. Division of all the figures by a common number will reduce the size but maintain proportion. If, for instance, all the square roots in Fig. 99 are divided by 25, radii range from 15.0 mm to

Fig. 98 *Proportional circles to illustrate the decline in herring landings between 1974 and 1979. An alternative scale is shown in diagram b.*

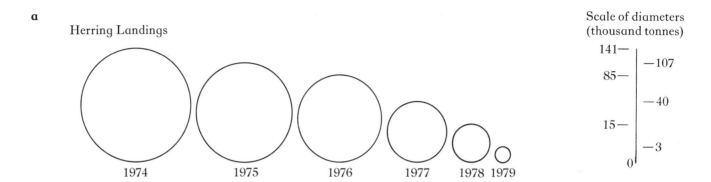

a

Herring Landings

1974 1975 1976 1977 1978 1979

Scale of diameters
(thousand tonnes)

141—
85—
15—
0

—107
—40
—3

b

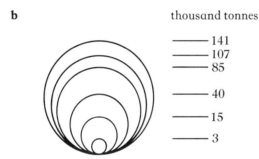

thousand tonnes

——— 141
——— 107
——— 85
——— 40
——— 15
——— 3

Fig. 99 *A table to aid calculation of the radii of proportional circles*

	Tonnes	$\sqrt{}$
1974	141 000	375.5
1975	107 000	327.1
1976	85 000	291.5
1977	40 000	200.0
1978	15 000	122.5
1979	3000	54.8

2.2 mm, and these are the dimensions of the circles in Fig. 98. Size must, therefore, be considered with care and the lowest value is usually critical. Student compasses seldom have the precision to cope with radii of less than three millimetres. It may be noted that decimal radii are hard, if not impossible, to achieve in practice, but rounding off to the nearest millimetre gives an acceptable level of accuracy.

If proportional circles are to be fully interpreted, a scale is needed. Two examples are included in Fig. 98. For a), radii are doubled and stepped on a vertical line. In b), circles of the correct size are neatly nested. A third type is seen in Fig. 118 (page 76).

Proportional circles perform the same task as bars and can be compared for effectiveness. The circle is a pleasing rounded shape that is preferred by many to the stark and angular bar, but it does have its disadvantages. It is more tedious to construct and needs more space. The eye finds it difficult to distinguish between circles that differ only slightly in size, and so values are generally less easy to distinguish. When faced with a choice between circle and bar, the nature of the data, the purpose of the illustration and personal preference are factors to consider.

The circle is the basis of a popular diagram showing subdivision of a total. Fig. 100 is an example showing the 1970 landings of demersal species taken from Fig. 80. This *divided circle*, often entitled *pie graph* or *pie chart*, can only be used with percentage data. A preparatory table, Fig. 101, for instance, helps avoid careless errors. Percentages are calculated and inserted. They must then be translated into degrees. 100% of a circle is 360°. 1% is, therefore,

$$\frac{360°}{100} = 3.6°.$$

Hence, to fill the fourth column, the percentage figures are multiplied by 3.6. With columns completed, construction can commence. A circle of convenient size is drawn. Segments of appropriate size are worked out by protractor. It is conventional to start at 12 o'clock and deal with values in order of decreasing size.

Numerous small divisions are best avoided. Minor values can be grouped together under a heading of 'others'. Labelling may prove to be a problem. Large segments can hold their titles, but with narrow ones, it is advisable to name in the margin and locate by arrow. It should be possible to read the graph without rotating the circle. Appearance is

Fig. 100 *Pie graph to illustrate the landings of demersal species in 1970*

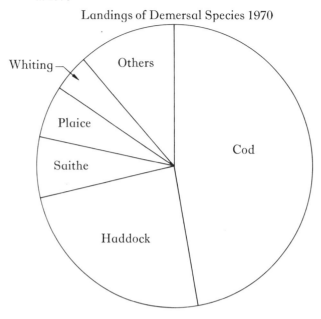

Landings of Demersal Species 1970

Fig. 102 *Proportional pie graphs to compare the landings of pelagic species in 1970 and 1979*

Landings of Pelagic Species

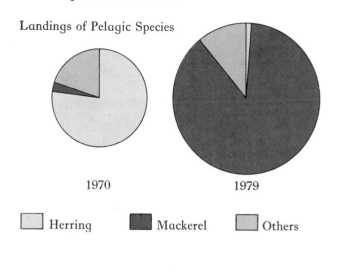

1970   1979

☐ Herring   ■ Mackerel   ☐ Others

Fig. 101 *Preparatory table for producing pie graph*

Fish	Thousand tonnes	%	Degrees
Cod	344	47.3	170
Haddock	176	24.2	87
Saithe	50	6.9	25
Plaice	44	6.0	22
Whiting	30	4.1	15
Others	83	11.4	41
Total	727		

Fig. 103 *Divided semicircles to illustrate the landings of demersal and pelagic fish in 1970*

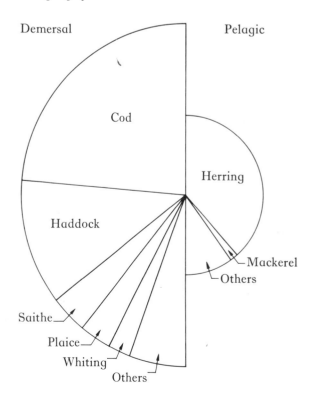

enhanced if segments are shaded, and if labelling is difficult, shading may form the basis of an explanatory key.

Two or more pie graphs may, of course, stand together to highlight comparisons between times or areas. If it is only the subdivision of totals that is of interest, then circles of equal size may be used, but the picture is often enhanced if the circles are made proportional. Fig. 102 uses landings of pelagic species to provide illustration.

Fig. 103 illustrates a variation on the theme. Here, semicircles are proportional to the 1970 landings of demersal and pelagic species. Radii are obtained in the manner described above but only half the circle is drawn against a vertical line. Semicircles are divided to show subdivisions of the total, but it must be remembered that 1% of a semicircle is 1.8°.

63

7 Use the data from Fig. 80 (page 53) to answer the following:

  a Illustrate, by proportional circles, the landings of cod for the years from 1970 to 1979. Compare your finished graph with Figs. 81 and 92. Comment on the relative merits of the three techniques.

  b Draw proportional divided circles (pie graphs) to illustrate landings of demersal species in 1970 and 1979.

  c Draw proportional semicircles to illustrate the contribution of the various demersal and pelagic species to total wet fish landings in 1979.

8 In the light of practical experience, and the study of examples, discuss the advantages and disadvantages of lines, bars and circles as means of representing geographical data.

Triangles

Triangles are well shaped to carry percentage data with three constituent parts. Fig. 104 is an example of a triangular graph. It uses data from Fig. 105.

The triangle is equilateral. Size can vary but sides of 10 cm (100 mm) will be found to be convenient. Each section of data is alloted a side divided into ten equal parts. Divisions are joined as seen in the example. Slight projections beyond the frame prove helpful when using the graph. With clockwise motion each side is scaled from 0 to 100. Note that each point of the triangle carries the 100 of one scale and the zero for the one that follows.

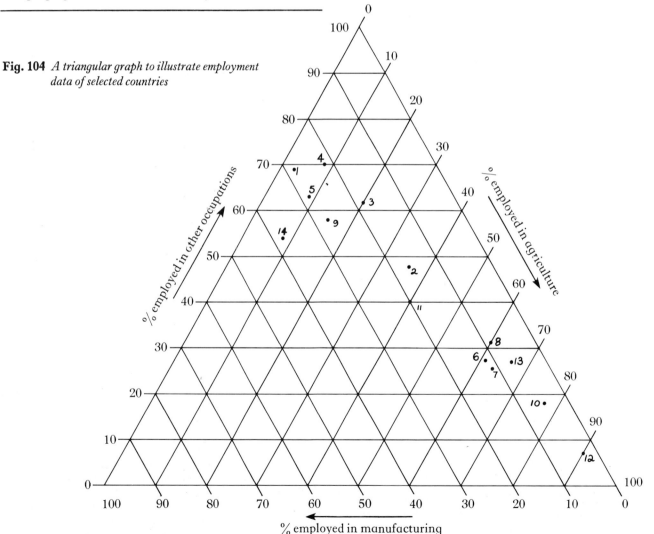

Fig. 104 *A triangular graph to illustrate employment data of selected countries*

Fig. 105 *Population and employment in selected countries*

	Country	Agriculture	Mining & manufacturing	Other	under 15	15 – 64	65 and over
		% of population employed in:			*% population*		
1	Belgium	3	28	69	23	63	14
2	Brazil	36	16	48	42	55	3
3	Chile	20	18	62	35	60	5
4	Denmark	9	21	70	23	64	13
5	France	9	28	63	24	62	14
6	Honduras	61	12	27	47	51	2
7	India	64	11	25	40	57	3
8	Indonesia	60	9	31	43	54	3
9	Italy	15	27	58	24	64	12
10	Liberia	77	5	18	42	55	3
11	Mexico	40	20	40	46	51	3
12	Rwanda	90	4	6	44	53	3
13	Sierra Leone	66	8	26	42	55	3
14	Switzerland	8	38	54	22	65	13

Estimates: mid 1970s

Reading from, or plotting on, a triangular graph may need a little practice, and here the projections included in the construction will serve as helpful pointers. Take Mexico (11), for example. Its position lies at the intersection of the lines representing 40% (agriculture), 20% (manufacturing) and 40% (other). For percentages not in neat and convenient units of 10, measurement or, more usually, estimation is required. In the case of Chile, this would lead to 20%, 18% and 62%. Consider the locations of other countries on Fig. 104. Jot down your estimates and check with Fig. 105.

Fig. 104 merits another glance. The distribution of dots leads to the identification of two distinct clusters. Dependence on agriculture draws developing countries down to the bottom right-hand corner. Advanced countries, with highly developed tertiary activities, cluster in a different part of the graph. Grouping and classification is an important function of the triangular graph.

9 Draw a triangular graph to illustrate the population data given in Fig. 105.

Radii

Radii are particularly useful when data has a directional component. The wind-rose is the most commonly encountered variety of the *vector diagram*. It is seen in its most simple form in Fig. 106. The length of the radii are proportional to wind frequency. The number of *calms* is recorded in the central circle. Fig. 106 is drawn from observation each day at 09.00 h for a single month. Other possibilities include monthly or annual means. The diagram could be adapted for percentage data, and expanded to serve sixteen compass points. Greater impact may be achieved if radii are replaced by slender bars. These may be readily divided and keyed to record associated data such as precipitation or visibility.

When directional data is available in the form of angular measurement, grouping is usually necessary. A simple example would be for all bearings between $337\frac{1}{2}°$ and $022\frac{1}{2}°$ to be scaled on a line or bar projecting northward; all between $022\frac{1}{2}°$ and $067\frac{1}{2}°$ are indicated as North East, and so on around the compass. An example where this method was employed is given in Fig. 107, which records the direction of movement involved in moving house by a sample of families in a large northern town. Here, the central circle is a cosmetic device to avoid clutter at the focus of bars.

The trend of linear features is recorded in angular bearings ranging from 000° to 179° (see page 25). Here again, grouping is necessary for appropriate illustration. Fig. 108 is based on the reasonably reliable results of student investigation into the orientation of rock fragments in a deposit of boulder clay. A class interval of 20° was chosen. The number of fragments in each class is scaled on the mid-class radius. The number between 000° and 019°, for instance, is scaled on a radius drawn at 010°. Each scaled

Fig. 106 *A wind-rose to show frequency and direction recorded over a period of one month*

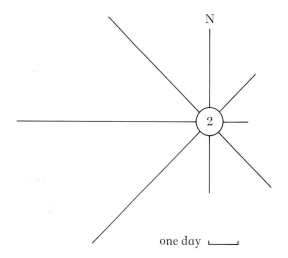

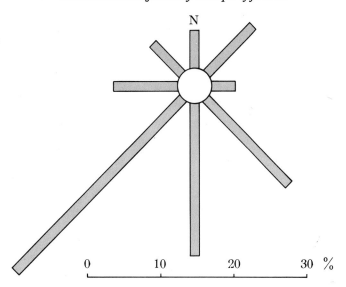

Fig. 107 *A vector diagram to record the direction of movement involved in moving house by a sample of families*

N

0   10   20   30 %

radius is extended through the origin for an equal distance. The ends of the radii are joined and light shading provides emphasis. In Fig. 108 the pecked lines represent original construction lines.

10 Draw a simple vector diagram to illustrate the data used in question 6, (page 50).

11 Measurement of the orientation of a group of cirques produced the following data:

Orientation	000°–044°	045°–089°	090°–134°	135°–179°
No. of cirques	9	6	3	1
Orientation	180°–224°	225°–269°	270°–314°	315°–360°
No. of cirques	1	2	1	5

Express this data in the form of:
a a vector diagram;
b a histogram.
Which technique do you consider most effectively illustrates the data?

Fig. 108 *A vector diagram used to illustrate the orientation of rock fragments in a deposit of boulder clay*

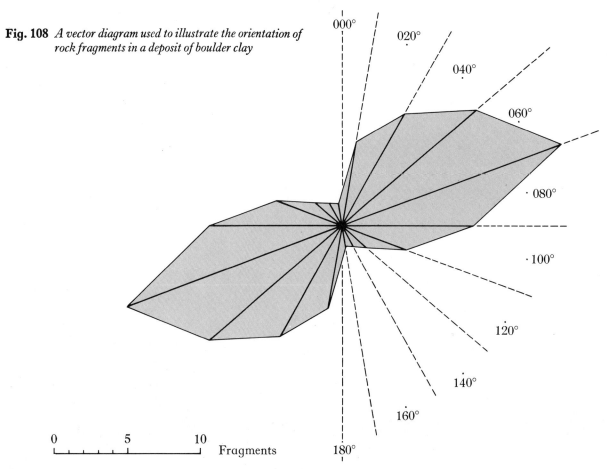

000°
020°
040°
060°
· 080°
· 100°
120°
140°
160°
180°

0   5   10   Fragments

Lorenz Curve

Population, a phenomenon of great interest to the geographer, typically shows an uneven distribution within area, region or country. The *Lorenz curve* gives a visual impression of this unevenness.

Belgium will provide an example. Construction demands data in the form seen in Fig. 109. It is important to note that constituent parts (in this case provinces) are listed in decreasing order of population. Fig. 110 gives the standard framework for the Lorenz curve. Cumulative percentages are the co-ordinates, and plotted points are smoothly joined to give the curve.

Readings may be taken from the curve. From Fig. 110 it can be seen that 40% of Belgium's population is concentrated on 21% of its area. Similarly 50% of the area of the country supports 74% of the population.

Fig. 109 *Preparatory table for producing a Lorenz curve*

Province	Population (%)	Cumulative %	Area (%)	Cumulative %
Brabant	22.6	22.6	10.8	10.8
Antwerp	15.9	38.5	9.2	20.0
E. Flanders	13.5	52.0	9.6	29.6
Hainault	13.5	65.5	12.2	41.8
W. Flanders	10.9	76.4	12.0	53.8
Liege	10.4	86.8	12.5	66.3
Limburg	7.0	93.8	7.8	74.1
Namur	4.0	97.8	11.8	85.9
Luxembourg	2.2	100.0	14.1	100.0

Fig. 110 *Lorenz curves to compare the distribution of population in Belgium and Sweden*

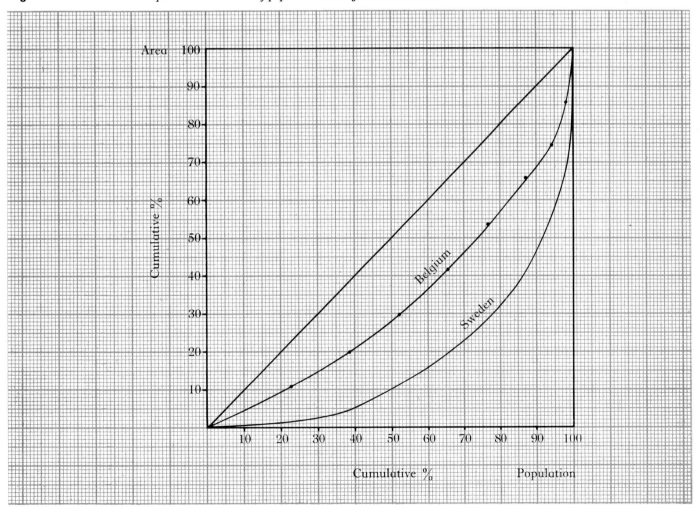

Note the diagonal that bisects Fig. 110. This is the curve of a perfectly even distribution, that is, one with no degree of concentration. This diagonal should always be included to serve as a standard of comparison. The more the plotted curve departs from the diagonal, that is, the greater its concavity, the more uneven is the distribution, or, expressed another way, the greater is the degree of concentration. The inclusion of the curve for Sweden in Fig. 110 illustrates the role the Lorenz curve can play in the making of comparisons.

The visual impression provided by the Lorenz curve may, at the cost of a little calculation, be translated into a numerical index. This *concentration ratio* is obtained by dividing the area between curve and diagonal by the area below the diagonal. Measurement of area need not be too arduous if the curve is drawn on graph paper and the method outlined on page 26 is followed. The ratio ranges from 0 to 1. A low value indicates an even distribution. If the ratio is close to 1, population is highly concentrated in a small part of the total area.

It must be borne in mind that each of the provinces of Belgium encompasses areas of contrasting population density, hence the picture may only be an outline. Greater accuracy is achieved by increasing the number of areal units employed.

The Lorenz curve is not restricted to population data. It may profitably be used with a variety of phenomena which vary with area. Industrial employment and land use are two examples.

Consolidation

Use the tabled data for Commonwealth migration to answer the questions.

Commonwealth migration into and out of Britain (thousands)

Year	Total	Australia	Canada	New Zealand	Africa	Bangladesh, India & Sri Lanka	West Indies	Other
Immigrants								
1969	116	25	13	7	16	32	10	13
1970	121	31	15	7	20	27	7	14
1971	116	31	13	7	27	24	5	9
1972	130	31	11	6	44	23	5	10
1973	99	31	11	7	22	11	5	12
1974	89	22	7	10	18	11	4	17
1975	100	26	7	10	21	13	5	18
1976	93	24	7	8	18	15	4	17
1977	74	20	6	8	14	11	4	11
1978	81	18	6	9	13	19	4	12
1979	90	16	6	9	16	19	5	19
Emigrants								
1969	181	95	33	9	16	10	9	9
1970	169	87	27	11	19	10	8	7
1971	134	69	15	13	15	8	8	6
1972	131	56	17	15	15	12	7	9
1973	138	55	28	25	12	5	7	6
1974	156	63	36	28	13	4	6	6
1975	107	29	36	14	13	3	4	8
1976	90	31	22	9	11	4	3	10
1977	91	32	18	8	16	4	3	10
1978	73	25	14	9	10	4	2	9
1979	75	23	18	8	9	4	3	10

Adapted from Annual Abstract of Statistics

12 Illustrate migration from Britain to Canada from 1969 to 1979 by: **a** linear graph; **b** three-year running mean.

13 Choose *two* contrasting techniques to illustrate, for 1975:
a the % origin of commonwealth immigrants into Britain;
b the % destination of emigrants from Britain.

14 For each of the years 1969 and 1979 use *two* contrasting methods to illustrate:
a the origin of immigrants;
b the destination of emigrants.

15 Select *three* different diagrammatic techniques to illustrate total commonwealth immigration into Britain from 1969 to 1979. Discuss the relative merits of the techniques employed.

16 Calculate the balance of total migration (+ or −) from 1969 to 1979. Illustrate your figures by appropriate linear and bar graphs. Which do you consider the most suitable technique?

17 Use *three* different techniques to illustrate total emigration and the destination of emigrants from Britain from 1969 to 1979. Comment on the advantages and limitations of the techniques employed.

18 Use divided semicircles to illustrate total migration and the origin/destination of migrants in 1974.

19 Using data of population and area from Fig. 2 (page 5) draw Lorenz curves for Teesdale parishes groups A and B. Compare the curves and comment on any contrast.

Section E · Statistical Mapping

The geographer has a fundamental interest in the spatial variation of phenomena both human and physical. Evidence is often in the form of statistics, while the map encompasses space. The marriage of statistics and map gives geography a visual dimension.

Three questions are asked of the statistical map:

1. Does it give a true and accurate picture of a particular distribution?
2. Is the picture presented in a pleasing and attractive manner?

3. Can its statistical basis be interpreted with ease?

These are the criteria against which the map is judged. Statistical maps must always be viewed with a critical eye.

There are several types of statistical map in common use. None is perfect. Each has its strengths and its weaknesses. The map itself imposes constraints of scale and shape. All ideals are hard to achieve and compromise is often inevitable. An important part of the required skill lies in the choice of method.

Fig. 111 *Dot map to show, on a parish basis, the distribution of population in western Teesdale, 1981*

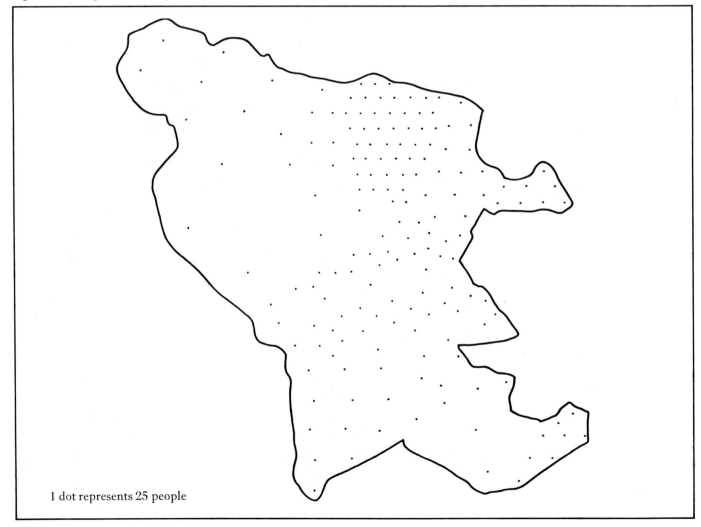

1 dot represents 25 people

Dot Maps

This type of map is a popular treatment for discrete (counted) data such as population, livestock and crop production. Fig. 111 is an example based on the population figures for the parishes of western Teesdale. The base map is traced from Fig. 1 (page 4). Pencilled parish boundaries form a framework. Each dot represents 25 people, and within each parish, dots are evenly spotted. For the finished map, internal boundaries may be inked or erased.

The eye is sensitive to varying density of dot. Concentration of population in the north-east of Fig. 111 is clearly evident, and gradations are discerned right down to the sparsely inhabited western fringe. Thus, the map gives a visual impression of the distribution of population in this rural corner of County Durham.

Although simple in concept, the dot map poses considerable problems in construction. Perhaps the greatest lies in dot value and size. Both affect the gradation of shade on the finished map and hence its appearance and usefulness. If the size is too large or the number too great, plotted dots may coalesce into ugly blotches. A small number of tiny dots may prove inadequate to the task of representing distribution. Often the problem may be solved only by patient trial and error. Test treatments of areas with the lowest and highest values will point to the wisest choice.

Regular spacing of dots is also difficult, especially if few in number and Fig. 111 may be criticised on this score. The eye is quick to light on any irregularity and finds them distracting. It is helpful if the map is drawn on a tracing

Fig. 112 *Dot map to show distribution of population in western Teesdale, 1981. Compare this map with Fig. 111*

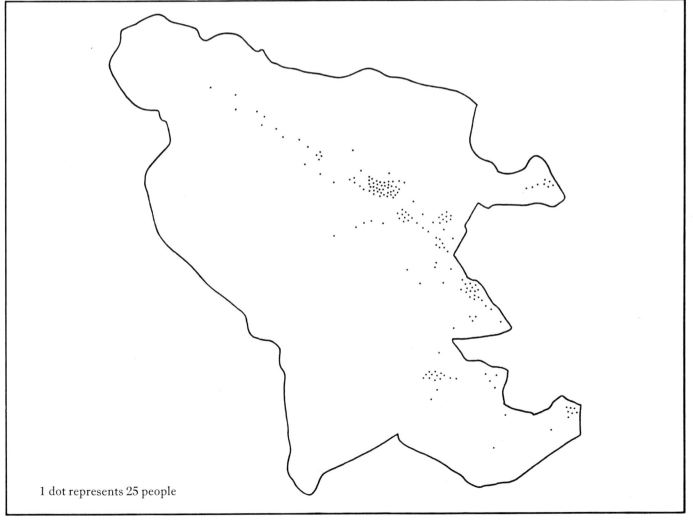

1 dot represents 25 people

sheet placed over graph paper, but care is essential, and preliminary pencil plotting is a wise practice. Uniform dots, moreover, are not easy to achieve. They demand drawing or lettering pens rather than the student's normal writing equipment.

The dot map has other weaknesses. Recall of data is neither easy nor accurate. With each dot worth 25, a parish of 35 souls has 10 unrepresented. The problem is greater as dot value increases. Counting is tedious and perhaps unreliable when dots are many. A more serious weakness is the inherent assumption that population is evenly distributed within the parish. This is seldom the case, so the map may fail to represent some significant subtleties of distribution.

However, too bleak a picture must not be painted. Constructional problems can be overcome. The dot map is seldom called upon to yield up the data on which it is based. Within its limitations, this flexible type of map may be used with a wide variety of data, and can give a broad but effective impression of a distribution.

In the above example, information was restricted to parish figures and form. When, as is often the case, further information is available, the dot technique gains useful stimulus. Fig. 112, like Fig. 111, covers western Teesdale. The size and value of dot is the same in each case, but the pictures are different. In constructing Fig. 112, use has been made of information available on the OS map, which, with its shading for settlement, records where people actually live. The dots due to each parish have been shared as fairly as possible between nucleated settlements and outlying farms. This involves subjective judgement, but the result is a distribution that is more in accord with reality. It highlights the pronounced contrast between the lower land along the Tees and the deserted upland rim.

In similar fashion, distributions of livestock and harvest can be more effectively portrayed if the topographical map is consulted for details of relief and vegetation.

A variation of the technique is to be noted. The dot may be given a percentage rather than a numerical value. If, for instance, each dot is worth 1% of the total, distribution is indicated by the location of 100 dots.

 Using tracings of Fig. 131 (page 94) as base maps, draw dot maps to illustrate, for Teesdale parishes group B, the distribution of:
a population;
b cattle and calves;
c sheep and lambs.
Obtain the necessary data from Figs. 2 and 127.

Choropleth

This impressive name is given to a familiar type of statistical map. Appropriate areas, usually administrative divisions, are treated with shading that is scaled to reflect differences within a distribution. The choropleth technique is not suitable for discrete data. Figures must be expressed as a ratio with area. Common examples include population density per km², livestock or crop yields per hectare, and percentage of land in agricultural use.

For an example—Fig. 113—we return again to western Teesdale. The subject this time is not population total but population density. The map is seen to make use of grouped data and herein lies the main problem with this type of map. The choice of class division is critical, for it greatly influences the appearance and message of the finished map. It merits careful and thoughtful consideration. In theory, there is no limit to the number of divisions, but as the number increases, problems of shading and interpretation multiply. In practice, 4, 5 or 6 divisions are usually adequate. As a preliminary, careful examination of the data is essential. It is best viewed in rank order, and a dispersion graph (page 13) may be helpful here. There are various bases for division. It can be arithmetical, for instance, rising in equal units of, say, 10 or 100. Geometrical progression is popular for maps of population density, and Fig. 113 is constructed on this basis. A four-fold grouping, based on medians and quartiles, is commonly encountered. Irregular groupings are also possible, and pleasing when they correspond to natural breaks in a sequence of figures. Final choice will depend upon the nature of the data, and the effect desired of the map. Vacant classes are best avoided.

Having fixed the number of classes, the next decision is the range of shading. Ideally, shading should progress smoothly from light to dark. Blank and black are best avoided. An unshaded area suggests an absence of value which may not be the case. Solid black may over-emphasise a value or obscure the map. Colour presents problems. A gradual range of tints is hard to achieve with student materials and a jump to another colour is disconcerting. Probably the best solution is line shading, and an example that covers eight classes is given in Fig. 114a. By elimination of extremes it is readily adapted to fewer required classes. It claims to give the required gradation, and permits easy identification. Graded densities of dots are another possibility, but tend to be tedious to draw and hard to interpret. Nevertheless, dots are included in Fig. 114b for they can, in moderation, be useful in showing an exceptional plus or minus value. Students may, of course, test their ingenuity by developing their own range of shading. A common error to be avoided is seen in Fig. 115, where lines vary in direction but not in density.

For perfect results, lines must be precisely parallel. This is not as daunting a task as may be feared, for help is available.

Fig. 113 *A choropleth map to show population density in western Teesdale, 1981*

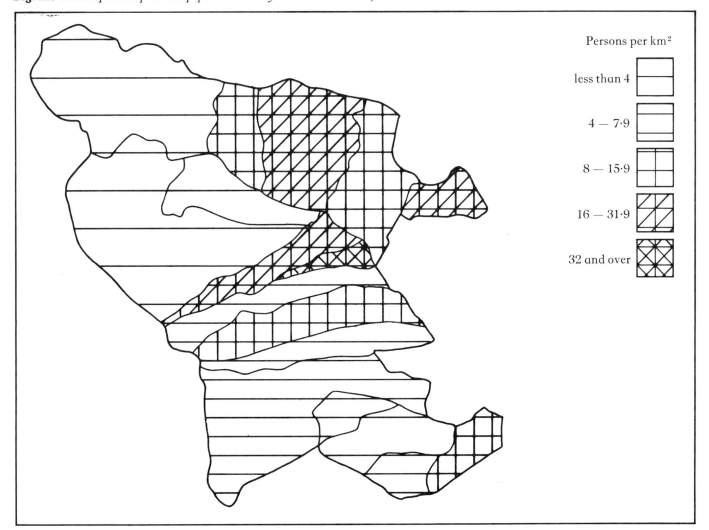

Persons per km²

less than 4

4 — 7·9

8 — 15·9

16 — 31·9

32 and over

If the map is to be drawn on tracing paper, a graph-paper underlay is a tremendous asset. When tracing paper is not acceptable, as in an examination, for instance, the practical experience of the following example may prove useful. The map outlined in Fig. 116 is to be shaded with a five-class scale (2 to 6 in Fig. 114). It is framed with sides marked off in 2–mm divisions. Small numbers indicate the class of shading required. Trace Fig. 116 and take the following steps. Using alternate side markings, draw lines right across the full map area. Next, working systematically from top to bottom, draw intermediate horizontal lines over all areas

except those marked 1. Areas marked 3, 4 and 5 are now treated to alternate vertical lines keyed to scale on the top and bottom of the frame. Then, areas 4 and 5 jointly receive a diagonal. Finally, group 5, the group of highest value, is given a second diagonal. Frame and numbers may then be erased.

Examine Fig. 113 again with a view to evaluation. It reveals at a glance that there is considerable variation in population density within this relatively small area, and quick recourse to the key reveals, at least approximately, the degree of this variation. On the other hand, variation within

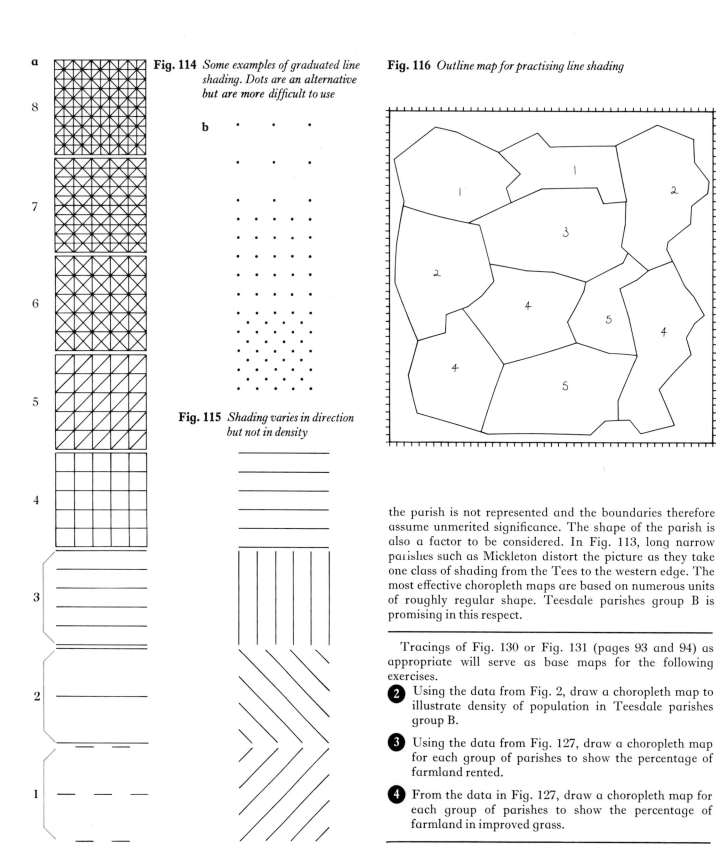

Fig. 114 *Some examples of graduated line shading. Dots are an alternative but are more difficult to use*

Fig. 115 *Shading varies in direction but not in density*

Fig. 116 *Outline map for practising line shading*

the parish is not represented and the boundaries therefore assume unmerited significance. The shape of the parish is also a factor to be considered. In Fig. 113, long narrow parishes such as Mickleton distort the picture as they take one class of shading from the Tees to the western edge. The most effective choropleth maps are based on numerous units of roughly regular shape. Teesdale parishes group B is promising in this respect.

Tracings of Fig. 130 or Fig. 131 (pages 93 and 94) as appropriate will serve as base maps for the following exercises.

2 Using the data from Fig. 2, draw a choropleth map to illustrate density of population in Teesdale parishes group B.

3 Using the data from Fig. 127, draw a choropleth map for each group of parishes to show the percentage of farmland rented.

4 From the data in Fig. 127, draw a choropleth map for each group of parishes to show the percentage of farmland in improved grass.

Isoline

An *isoline*, also known as an *isopleth*, is a line drawn on a map joining points which share a common value. They can be drawn for any phenomenon for which values at specific locations are available. Often they carry their own brand name. The familiar contour is an isoline joining all points at the same height above mean sea-level. Many other examples will be encountered. They abound in climatology: isotherms, isobars, isohyets and isohels are isolines of temperature, pressure, rainfall and sunshine respectively.

The first constructional requirement is a base map giving point locations of values. Then, the isoline interval must be selected. An arithmetical interval is the one most commonly employed, but geometrical, and, if the data shows natural breaks, irregular intervals may be chosen. The isoline interval controls the number of isolines that the map must carry. Too few may not do justice to the data: too many may clutter the map and so obscure the distribution.

The technique of isoline drawing is illustrated with the help of the simple example given as Fig. 117. It is clear that the isoline of 50 must pass through the three points so marked, but what of its course between them? This must be interpolated with regard to neighbouring values and the acceptable assumption that the rate of change is constant between them. Thus in Fig. 117, 50 can be assumed to lie half way between 60 and 40 and one third of the distance between 60 and 30. Precise measurement is not normally necessary, for estimation by eye gives an acceptable level of accuracy. Interpolated values are marked by light pencil crosses, and dots and crosses are joined in the smooth pencil curve that is the required isoline.

Place a piece of tracing paper over Fig. 117 and insert the isolines for 60, 40 and 30.

Errors will be avoided if it is firmly noted that isolines may never touch or cross. When all isolines have been positioned in pencil, they can be neatly inked and labelled. Constructional crosses are erased. Clarity is enhanced if the finished map does not carry the distraction of the original data.

The spaces between isolines may be shaded in the manner appropriate to choropleth maps (page 74). This gives greater visual impact, but as emphasis shifts from line to area, a stepped effect is produced, and this may damage the impression of transitional change that is a useful feature of this type of map.

The isoline is a popular form of statistical mapping. Spatial distribution is effectively portrayed and the statistical basis is not hidden from view. Many types of data can profit from isoline treatment, including measurements made in the field.

5 The sketch represents the results of a sample investigation into the depth of water in a small section of stream channel. Trace the channel limits and draw isolines for depths of 10 and 20 cm.

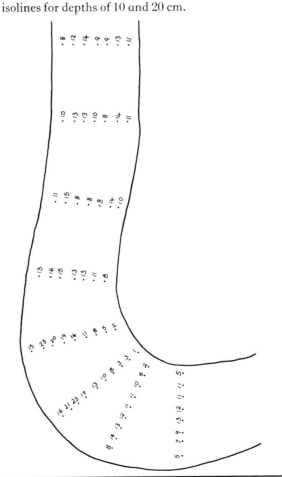

Fig. 117 *Drawing isolines*

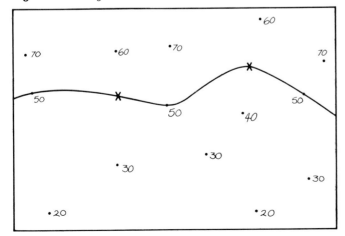

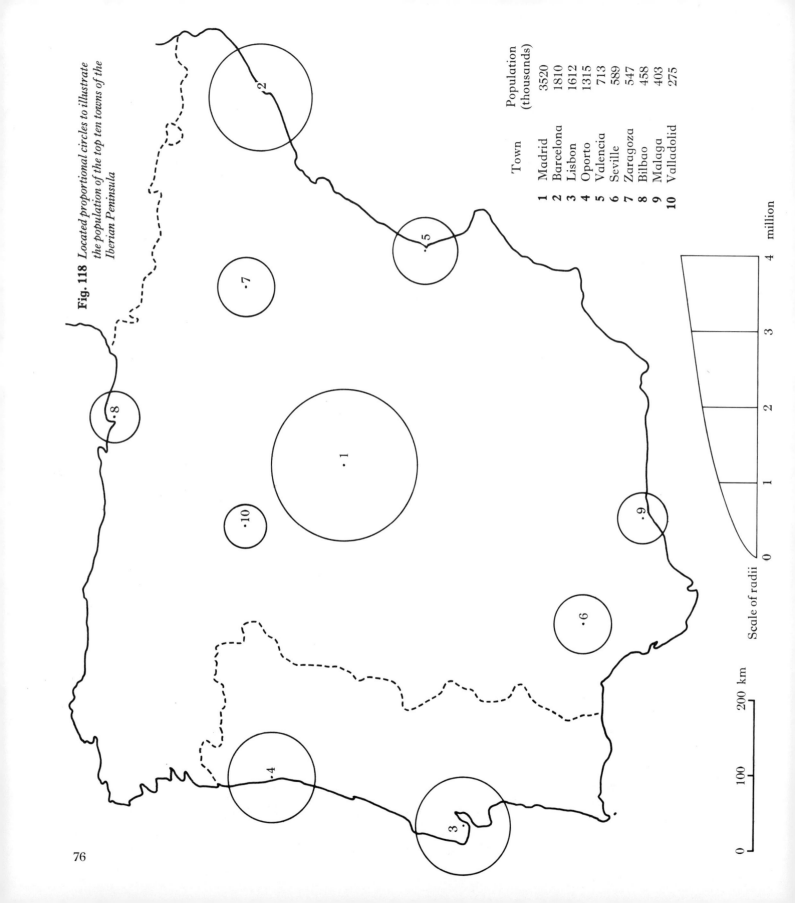

Fig. 118 *Located proportional circles to illustrate the population of the top ten towns of the Iberian Peninsula*

Town		Population (thousands)
1	Madrid	3520
2	Barcelona	1810
3	Lisbon	1612
4	Oporto	1315
5	Valencia	713
6	Seville	589
7	Zaragoza	547
8	Bilbao	458
9	Malaga	403
10	Valladolid	275

Scale of radii

0   1   2   3   4   million

0   100   200 km

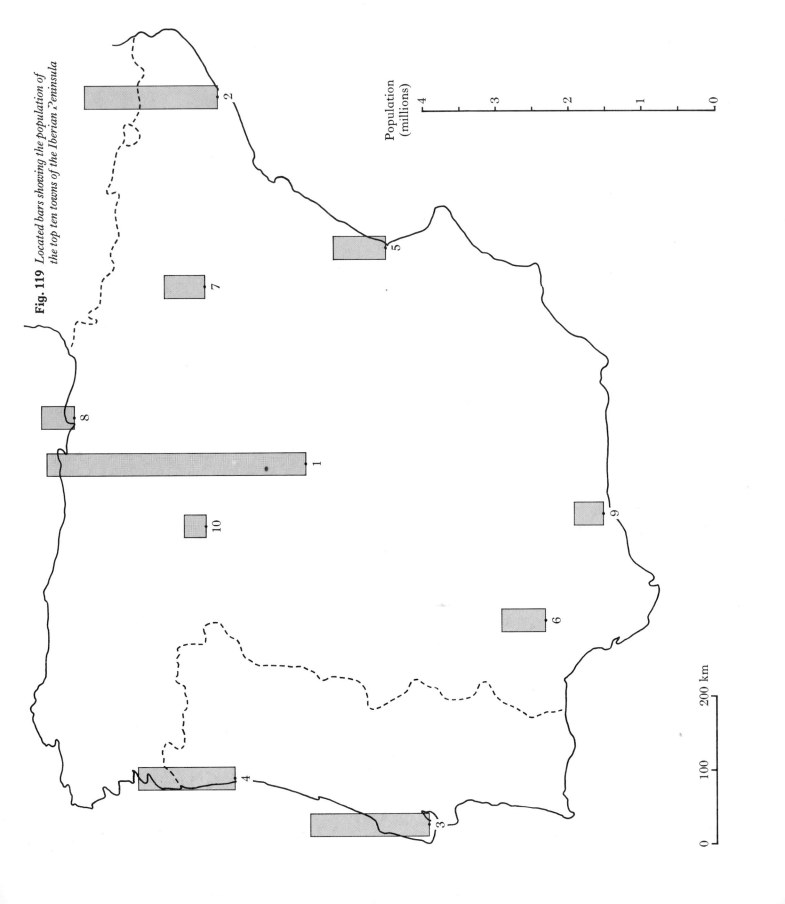

Fig. 119 *Located bars showing the population of the top ten towns of the Iberian Peninsula*

Population (millions)

4

3

2

1

0

200 km

0   100   200

Located Graphs and Diagrams

Section D (page 53) discusses a range of graphs and diagrams which give visual expression to a set of statistics. Careful location on a suitable base map offers the additional dimension of distribution. Location must overcome constraints of scale and shape and the finished map must tell its story with clarity, yet appeal to the eye.

Of the range of available graphs and diagrams, the most commonly used are circles and bars. In their simplest form they feature in Figs. 118 and 119. Both maps use the same statistics. Both give location and population of the top ten towns of the Iberian Peninsula. Comparison reveals relative advantages. With bars, the centre of the base is the point of location and the rising column takes the eye away from the site of the town. In Fig. 118, centres of circles and towns coincide, so it can claim to reflect location more effectively. The inclusion of a scale on each map permits populations to be determined, but the simple linear scale of the bar has the edge in speed and accuracy. Assessment of map appeal is a subjective judgement. Which do you find most pleasing?

When large towns, or indeed, any phenomena, are closely clustered, problems of location arise. Solutions, less than ideal, but tolerable, are suggested in Fig. 120.

When statistics relate to areas rather than points, location of graphs and diagrams frequently meet difficulties imposed by the size and shape of administrative or other units. Ideally, each should fit neatly within the appropriate boundaries. Sadly, this is not always possible, since small areas may have high values and so earn large circles or bars. Overlapping of boundaries is often inevitable and, within limits, must be accepted. The finished map is a compromise, the one judged best in the circumstances.

Fig. 121 is an attempt to show by means of divided proportional circles the number and size of landholdings in the parishes of western Teesdale. The problems posed by size and shape are clearly evident. The student is left to judge the effectiveness of the map in the light of these problems. Can improvements be suggested? Are there alternative—and better—ways of presenting the data?

The simple examples above have been treated to illustrate basic technique. The student is reminded that a variety of graphs and diagrams is available. Wise and appropriate choice is most important. Which is most fitting to data and map? Judgement will be sharpened if examples contained in atlas and textbook are studied with a critical eye. The following exercises will pose problems that invite solutions.

Fig. 120 *Overlapping circles (a) and the use of arrows (b) are two solutions to the problem of representing clustered phenomena*

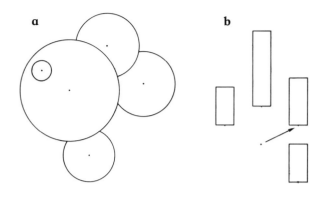

Tracings of Fig. 130 or Fig. 131 (pages 93 and 94), as appropriate, will serve as base maps for the following exercises.

6 Draw maps of Teesdale parishes group A to illustrate the data for population (Fig. 2) by means of:
   a located bars;
   b located proportional circles.

7 Draw maps of Teesdale parishes group A to illustrate the total number of cattle and calves (Fig. 127) by means of:
   a located bars;
   b located proportional circles.

8 Use the technique of located bars to illustrate, for Teesdale parishes group A, the percentage population change 1971 to 1981 (Fig. 2).

9 Draw maps of Teesdale parishes group B to illustrate the % of land rented (Fig. 127) by means of:
   a located divided circles;
   b located bars.

10 In the light of experience gained from the above exercises, discuss the relative merits of circles and bars as means of mapping statistical information.

Fig. 121 *Located proportional divided circles (pie graphs) to show the number and size of landholdings in the parishes of western Teesdale*

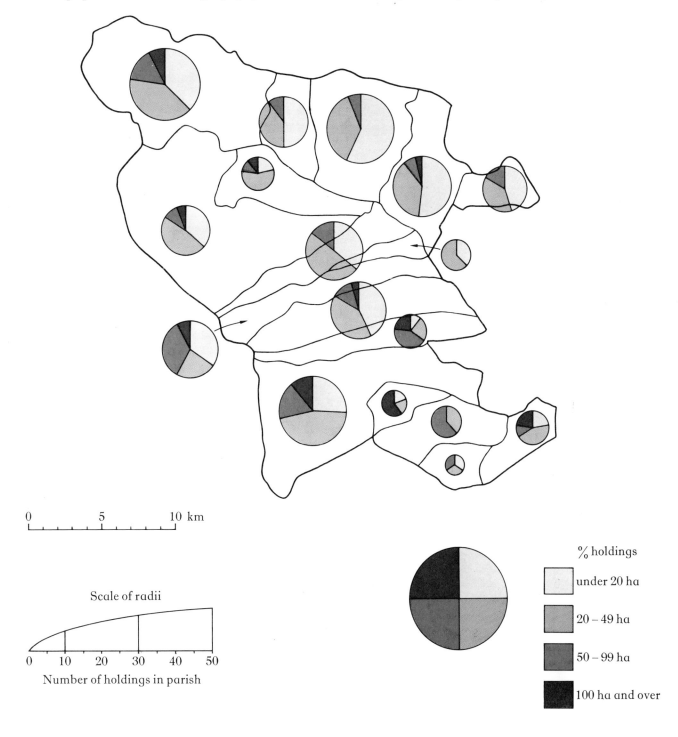

0   5   10 km

Scale of radii

0 10 20 30 40 50
Number of holdings in parish

% holdings

under 20 ha

20 – 49 ha

50 – 99 ha

100 ha and over

Flow Lines

Maps are wrinkled with lines of movement. Roads and railways, sea lanes and airways are cases in point. A *flow line* is simply a line of movement thickened in proportion to the traffic it bears.

Skipton is a busy market town in the Craven district of North Yorkshire. Bus services to the north and west of the town will illustrate the flow-line technique. The local bus time-table provides the relevant information. Routes are identified on and traced from a map of convenient scale. Awkward curves and corners are smoothed away to ease construction at a later stage. Careful counting yields the weekly total of buses passing over each section of each route. This information is pencilled on the traced base map.

The most challenging task is the choice of a suitable scale. If the scale is too small, flow lines are thin and the map lacks detail and emphasis. With scale too large, thick flow lines bring great confusion at a focus of routes and overwhelm the map when the network is dense. A balance is not easy to achieve—often it demands patient trial and error. Focal points are critical points. In Fig. 122, three busy routes converge on Skipton. A circle creates space, but the routes must still be comfortably accommodated on the circumference. Select with care the maximum convenient width of flow line, for this controls the scale. If this is to be directly proportional, a triangle scale such as that included in Fig. 122 is helpful. A base of modest length is calibrated. The upright side rises as high as the chosen maximum width of flow line. For any particular value, the required width is the vertical distance between base and hypotenuse. A proportional scale is precise and effective but difficulty may be experienced when values are low. A suggested solution is to use a symbol—a pecked line, for instance—for all routes that carry less than, say, ten buses per week.

As an alternative to a proportional scale, traffic may be classed and routes awarded a line of appropriate thickness. A suggestion is seen in Fig. 123.

With scale decided, routes are thickened into flow lines. When lines are straight, this task is straightforward. Half the required width is marked on each side of the route and the marks are joined with a ruler. Narrow flow lines may be drawn to one side of the route. Curves are a little tricky, but a pair of compasses can be helpful. Follow the route with the point, and the pencil will trace the parallel. Special care is needed where routes converge.

Finally, the map is inked, construction lines and data are erased and flow lines shaded; scale and title must of course be added.

Fig. 122 *A flow-line map to show bus journeys per week in the Skipton area*

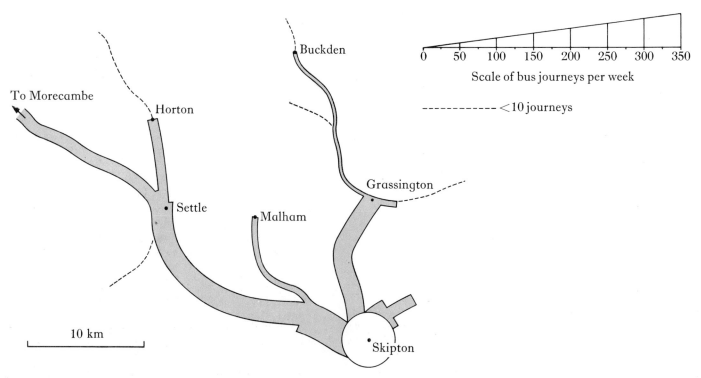

Fig. 123 *Lines of appropriate thickness are an alternative to the proportional scale used in Fig. 122*

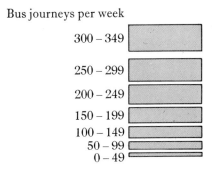

Bus journeys per week

300 – 349
250 – 299
200 – 249
150 – 199
100 – 149
50 – 99
0 – 49

The use of the flow line is not restricted to mere totals of buses and trains, ships and planes. Data of passengers carried and the value or tonnage of goods transported may be effectively illustrated by this technique, which may also serve for traffic and pedestrian flows.

11 With the help of local map and timetable, draw a flow-line map of bus services in your home area.

Desire Lines

Fig. 124 is a matrix of data relating to the movement of population between the standard regions of Britain. It tables movement. It reveals, for instance, that in 1980, 22 000 people left Scotland for new homes in the South East. 15 000 people did the reverse. Various forms of transport were involved and a diversity of routes followed. The data records total movement between region and region and does not relate to a particular line of communication. The flow line is therefore inappropriate. A close relative, the *desire line*, is used instead.

In Fig. 125 we see data mapped. Desire lines have widths determined in the manner described for flow lines. They must link area with area, but precise location is a matter of choice. Straight lines are generally most effective, but curves are often inevitable to avoid congestion. The aim is to produce a map that is accurate, clear and appealing.

12 Using the data provided by Fig. 124, and tracings of the standard regions in Fig. 125, draw maps to illustrate:
  a movement of population *from* the East Midlands to all other regions;
  b movement of population *to* the South West from all other regions.
  c *net* movement of population between the South East and all other regions.

Fig. 124 *Movement of population between the standard regions of Britain*

Inter-regional movements 1980 (thousands)

Region of Destination \ Region of Origin	North	Yorkshire & Humberside	East Midlands	East Anglia	South East	South West	West Midlands	North West	Wales	Scotland
North	–	8	3	1	11	2	3	7	1	5
Yorkshire & Humberside	10	–	12	3	19	5	5	13	2	5
East Midlands	4	14	–	5	28	6	11	9	3	4
East Anglia	2	3	6	–	33	4	3	3	1	2
South East	15	22	24	24	–	50	27	30	15	22
South West	3	6	6	4	65	–	13	9	7	5
West Midlands	3	6	10	2	22	9	–	10	6	4
North West	7	12	7	2	21	6	10	–	7	7
Wales	1	3	3	1	15	6	7	10	–	1
Scotland	6	6	3	2	15	4	3	7	2	–

Regional Trends 1982

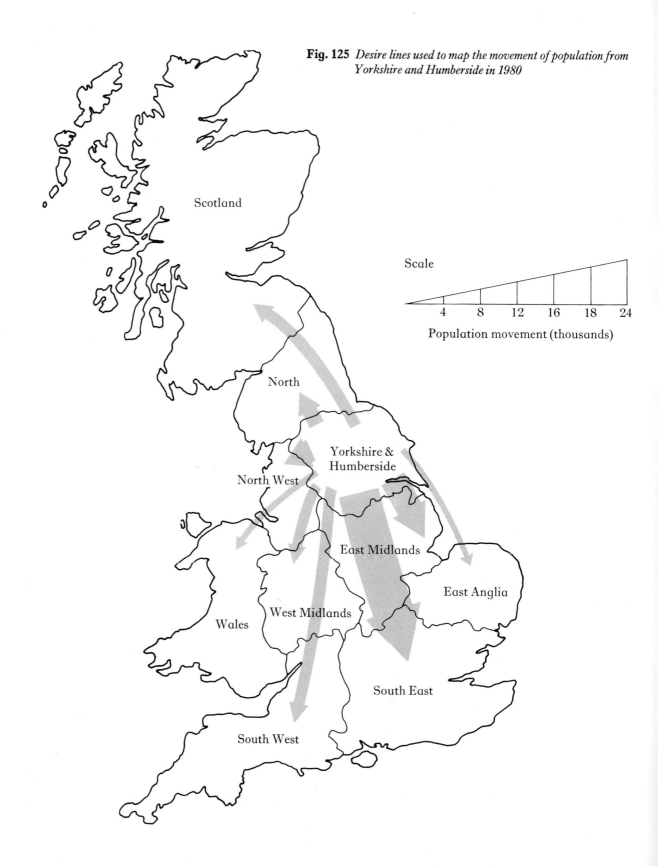

Fig. 125 *Desire lines used to map the movement of population from Yorkshire and Humberside in 1980*

Scotland

North

Yorkshire & Humberside

North West

East Midlands

East Anglia

Wales

West Midlands

South East

South West

Scale

4   8   12   16   18   24

Population movement (thousands)

Fig. 126 illustrates a further use of the desire line. The symbol locates the premises of a suburban fencing and paving contractor. The addresses he attended in the course of one year are marked by dots. Jobs are linked to base by fine desire lines. As each represents one link, they do not vary in width. The map gives a picture of a year's business activity. The bulk of his work lay within a 10-kilometre radius. Occasionally he travelled further afield, and clustering at these greater distances reflects the influence of personal recommendation.

Desire lines are frequently used in this way to illustrate catchment areas, zones of influence and urban fields. They are not restricted to journeys or movement. Linkages of any type may be used.

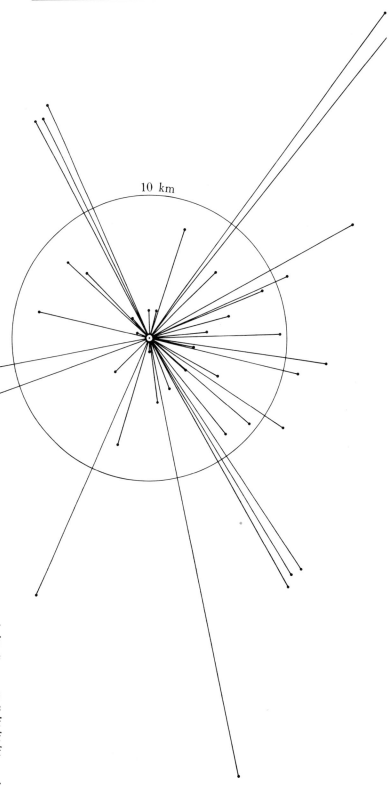

Fig. 126 *Desire lines used to plot job location of a contractor*

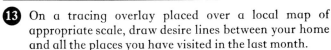

13 On a tracing overlay placed over a local map of appropriate scale, draw desire lines between your home and all the places you have visited in the last month.

14 Study a copy of your local newspaper. On a tracing overlay of a map of appropriate scale, draw desire lines joining the site of the publisher's office and the point of origin of all local news reports. Join the outer ends of all desire lines to give an indication of the field of influence.

Consolidation

Use data from Figs. 2 and 127 and tracings of Fig. 130 to answer the following questions.

15 Draw a dot map to illustrate the distribution of cattle in Teesdale parishes group A.

16 Draw a percentage dot map to show the distribution of sheep in Teesdale parishes group A.

17 Draw choropleth maps for Teesdale parishes group A to illustrate:
a cattle per 100 ha of farmland;
b percentage population change.

18 Using data from Fig. 124, and a tracing of the standard regions from Fig. 125, show on one map the movement of population *to* the South East from all other regions and the movement of population *from* the South East to all other regions.

19 The table gives selected statistical information for the regions of Italy shown on the map. Using in each case the technique you consider the most appropriate, map the following data sets:
a population;
b population density;
c birth rate;
d employment;
e unemployment rate;
f investment grants.

Region	Population 1980 (thousands)	Population density 1980 persons per km²	Births per 1000 population 1979	Employment 1979 % Agriculture	% Industry	% Services	Unemployment 1979 %	Investment grants 1980 (thousands European currency units)
Nord Ovest	6479	190	8.6	9	45	46	3.5	1463
Lombardia	8943	375	10.3	4	54	42	3.0	475
Nord Est	6478	163	10.3	9	43	48	3.1	10 676
Emilia-Romagna	3966	179	8.3	14	40	46	3.5	16 903
Centro	5829	142	9.5	12	41	47	3.7	15 128
Lazio	5074	295	11.7	6	26	68	7.4	10 606
Campania	5475	403	17.1	19	29	52	11.0	4410
Abruzzi-Molise	1577	104	12.4	26	30	44	5.7	5567
Sud	6632	149	16.3	24	26	50	8.9	31 726
Sicilia	5012	195	15.6	20	25	55	5.4	8259
Sardegna	1606	67	14.9	14	28	58	9.8	3904
ITALY	57 070	189	12.0	12	39	49	5.3	—

The table gives selected statistical information for the standard regions of Britain.

Choosing the most appropriate technique in each particular case, draw maps, on tracings of the regions from Fig. 125, of each of the following:

a population;
b population density;
c percentage population change 1961—1971 *and* 1971—1981;
d production of deep-mined coal;
e net population movement between regions;
f agricultural area and land use.

Region	Population (thousands) 1981	Population density persons per km²	Percentage population change 1961–71	Percentage population change 1971–81	Net population movement between regions (thousands) 1980	Production of deep-mined coal (million tonnes) 1980/81	Total agricultural land (thousand hectares) 1980	Land use % Crops	Land use % Grass	Land use % Rough grazing
North	3097	200	0.7	−1.4	−9	14.5	1058	17	51	31
Yorkshire & Humberside	4854	317	3.7	−0.1	−6	29.8	1104	49	36	12
East Midlands	3807	242	9.4	4.8	7	35.5	1243	62	33	3
East Anglia	1865	150	13.6	11.7	14	—	1014	81	13	2
South East	16 729	621	5.9	−1.2	1	0.8	1734	56	36	3
South West	4326	182	10.6	6.0	28	—	1849	25	66	6
West Midlands	5136	396	7.4	0.5	−10	8.9	982	37	57	2
North West	6406	880	2.6	−2.9	−21	4.0	456	20	66	13
Wales	2790	134	3.3	2.2	3	8.4	1512	7	67	24
Scotland	5117	65	1.0	−2.1	−8	7.7	5579	11	19	68

Fig. 127 *Agricultural data for Teesdale parishes groups A and B*

Teesdale Parishes **GROUP A** (June 1981)	Area of land in farms (hectares)	Percentage rented	Mean farm size (hectares)	Percentage land use			Farm type (part-time excluded)			Farm size (classified by standard man-days) Size groups (SMDs)				Total number of cattle & calves	Total number of sheep & lambs
				Rough grazing	Improved grass	Crops & fallow	Dairy	Livestock rearing & fattening	Other	<250 (part-time)	250–499	500–999	1000 and over		
1 Forest and Frith	4726	98	118.1	65	35	–	1	16	–	23	11	4	2	1874	15 121
2 Newbiggin	1302	97	65.1	59	41	–	1	10	–	9	9	2	–	1008	6515
3 Middleton-in-Teesdale	3122	43	84.4	76	24	–	3	10	1	23	11	3	–	1116	10 160
4 Eggleston	990	29	34.1	28	71	1	5	5	2	17	6	3	3	1030	9068
5 Woodland	1119	86	62.1	51	48	–	3	6	–	9	4	5	–	1037	3491
6 Lunedale	2937	92	154.6	78	22	–	–	11	–	8	5	6	–	822	12 119
7 Holwick	1485	94	165.0	69	30	–	1	6	–	2	4	2	1	919	7458
8 Mickleton	1180	37	42.1	36	64	–	4	4	–	20	5	3	–	1172	4410
9 Romaldkirk	223	30	27.9	22	77	–	1	1	–	6	1	1	–	349	389
10 Hunderthwaite	2681	48	103.1	56	43	–	6	11	–	9	8	9	–	1547	9668
11 Cotherstone	983	43	37.8	23	75	–	2	10	–	14	8	3	1	1326	8816
12 Lartington	1415	70	157.2	55	44	–	2	5	–	2	1	4	2	1088	5539
13 Bowes	3607	64	92.5	52	48	–	10	14	–	15	10	9	5	2946	21 024
14 Gilmonby	1036	4	207.2	57	43	–	1	1	1	2	–	–	3	686	4644
15 Scargill	940	98	117.5	54	43	1	2	6	–	–	2	6	–	881	4467
16 Hope	123	83	41.0	17	82	–	–	1	–	2	1	–	–	174	676
17 Barningham	795	85	88.3	29	57	12	1	3	–	5	–	3	1	713	4575

	Teesdale Parishes GROUP B (June 1981)	Area of land in farms (hectares)	Percentage rented	Mean farm size (hectares)	Percentage land use			Farm type (part-time excluded)			Farm size (classified by standard man-days) Size groups (SMDs)				Total number of cattle & calves	Total number of sheep & lambs
					Rough grazing	Improved grass	Crops & fallow	Dairy	Livestock rearing & fattening	Other	<250 (part-time)	250–499	500–999	1000 and over		
18	South Bedburn	1891	31	61.0	12	74	11	4	14	–	13	9	8	1	2136	8850
19	Hamsterley	743	25	27.5	4	90	5	2	4	2	19	6	1	1	872	2114
20	Lynesack & Softley	1494	38	24.5	8	89	1	12	5	2	42	10	8	1	3062	3749
21	Evenwood & Barony	1946	34	29.1	4	80	14	17	7	3	40	17	9	1	3342	3386
22	Etherley	1403	34	58.5	9	64	25	8	5	4	7	8	8	1	1688	2635
23	Langleydale & Shotton	1216	99	71.5	8	90	2	6	8	–	3	3	11	–	1785	7533
24	Cockfield	217	40	15.5	1	99	–	2	1	1	10	–	4	–	471	2661
25	Raby with Keverstone	1242	48	124.2	–	63	36	2	4	–	4	1	2	3	1291	6863
26	Wackerfield	421	52	60.1	1	45	53	2	1	1	3	2	1	1	480	552
27	Hilton	335	86	47.9	–	72	28	1	2	–	4	1	2	–	514	539
28	Bolam/Morton Tinmouth	369	27	52.7	6	75	18	1	2	1	3	1	3	–	533	1392
29	Marwood	2250	66	56.3	15	78	4	10	12	–	18	10	11	1	3321	9738
30	Streatlam & Stainton	740	45	56.9	3	90	6	2	6	2	3	5	2	3	1169	2889
31	Staindrop	716	59	39.8	3	69	28	6	2	2	8	3	5	2	1089	1767
32	Langton	219	100	73.0	12	51	36	2	–	1	–	2	1	–	284	402
33	Ingleton	297	70	21.2	1	69	29	2	–	1	11	–	2	1	431	703
34	Cleatlam	236	28	39.3	–	78	20	1	3	–	2	4	–	–	350	1028
35	Gainford/Headlam	1104	51	64.9	–	41	58	2	2	3	10	2	2	3	916	1607
36	Westwick	616	56	51.3	7	75	17	3	3	2	4	2	3	3	920	2194
37	Whorlton	1158	20	89.1	–	64	33	2	3	2	6	1	4	2	1316	4117
38	Winston	1079	52	77.1	3	66	29	3	5	–	6	2	4	2	1523	2379
39	Barforth/Ovington	809	30	53.9	2	40	54	–	3	6	6	5	4	–	527	2953
40	Boldron	635	56	45.4	30	69	–	6	–	–	8	2	3	1	879	2411
41	Startforth/Egglestone Abbey	410	50	51.3	2	74	23	1	2	–	5	2	1	–	535	804
42	Rokeby	574	91	82.0	–	40	59	1	1	4	1	4	1	1	473	1832
43	Wycliffe with Thorpe	629	44	69.9	2	46	48	1	2	1	5	2	2	–	450	754
44	Brignall	576	92	82.3	9	78	13	4	3	–	–	3	3	1	713	2189
45	Hutton Magna	481	89	160.3	–	41	59	–	2	1	–	1	1	1	263	1773

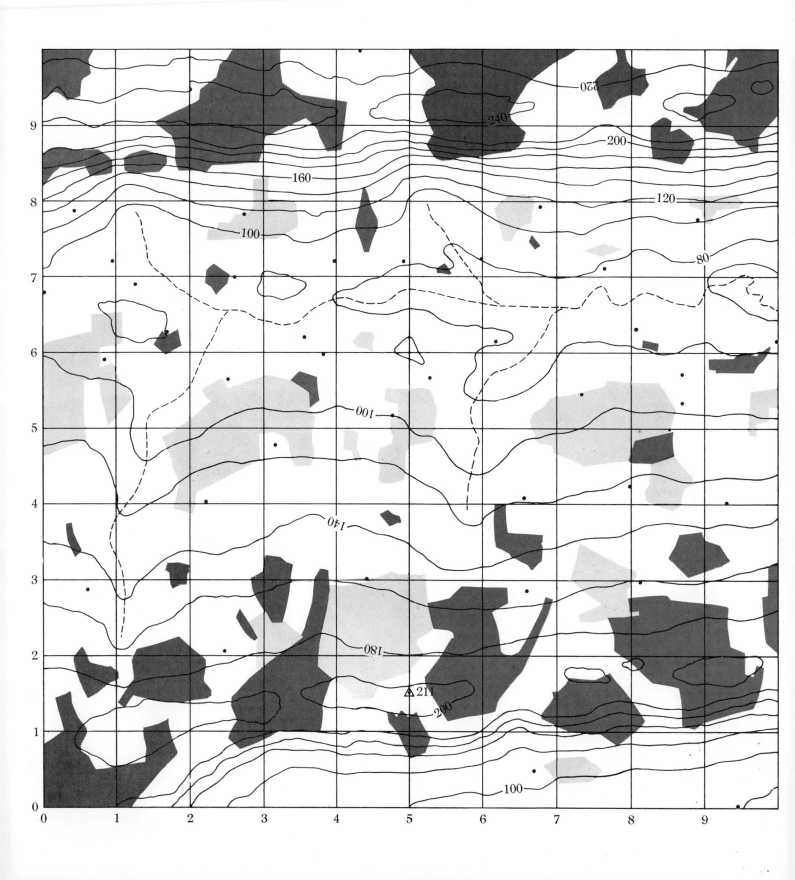

Fig. 128 *Land use map*

------ stream

•   farm

 orchard

 woodland

Fig. 129 *Random number tables*

```
3385 8358 5900 6614 1403 4467 7024 2582 8598 5372
3763 6794 8469 1015 6911 2144 0689 5969 5358 5157
6995 8197 2141 0277 3759 5250 3865 2182 2708 8965
6050 8358 8814 4082 1165 5870 8794 1589 8058 2643
3062 9095 0459 7128 8185 3707 2459 2052 0750 3454

8649 1915 0358 7235 9398 6135 7623 8071 5512 7435
8856 3649 3774 5375 8812 4375 8289 9870 1906 8154
6067 1781 9214 8442 5073 7940 9411 0199 8733 7934
6380 2632 7559 5368 0723 7796 2051 1696 7174 6682
8956 5021 6816 0609 2648 0782 2557 2830 3020 8554

1300 5502 6063 1934 6006 2692 1840 5686 8632 8563
1964 7340 0737 1028 2825 3685 2387 2251 7390 4157
7250 9621 6881 3234 9545 3507 4066 5417 6884 4073
5781 3934 1151 5808 7053 7824 4646 2673 2360 1130
7320 0586 5631 5563 5405 3015 4124 1974 2305 9824

6758 6787 2059 3176 8864 6704 7250 7219 3089 3975
5018 8643 5997 0334 6226 3341 8629 7333 6071 9251
1596 5539 3886 8218 9969 1188 2994 4922 0345 8435
0302 5302 6666 0424 8578 9669 3716 0929 7067 3445
4372 5842 9890 9205 7813 6482 0916 4270 1675 6867

9528 0203 3982 2016 5733 7369 3572 8067 8947 0359
1772 4460 3511 1131 7936 8508 6642 3012 5776 6664
1221 3960 6160 0937 6211 3204 3605 1011 1120 4250
7465 8241 0133 4488 8055 6276 3328 8922 0597 7899
5145 8529 2762 4059 7287 1685 9290 2378 9939 9702

9854 4850 7631 6458 2879 3442 2257 5853 5009 2865
5060 7856 3606 4505 1889 8374 6274 9475 1028 8908
2892 4636 9204 8696 1578 4259 5935 8487 5302 8837
5656 6625 0612 7104 9808 1159 5437 2026 1720 1713
3687 0703 9053 6829 0815 0430 8322 4416 5214 7255

3294 1351 8574 5273 1556 0796 7054 3879 1552 4872
1526 3444 6604 2194 6893 4333 0649 7239 1766 6428
3147 7406 3651 5324 7669 0420 0137 0697 5194 2457
6249 7836 4589 8370 4846 5713 2493 6527 0213 2090
8316 2772 7991 7585 7301 9847 0349 7400 6193 1120
```

Fig. 130 *Enlargement of Teesdale group A parishes*

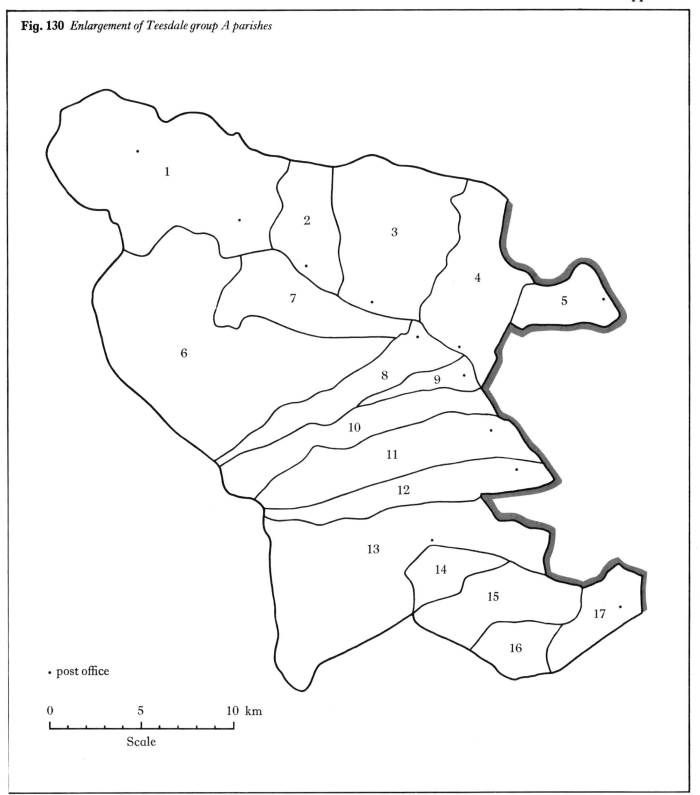

• post office

```
0          5          10  km
|——————————|——————————|
        Scale
```

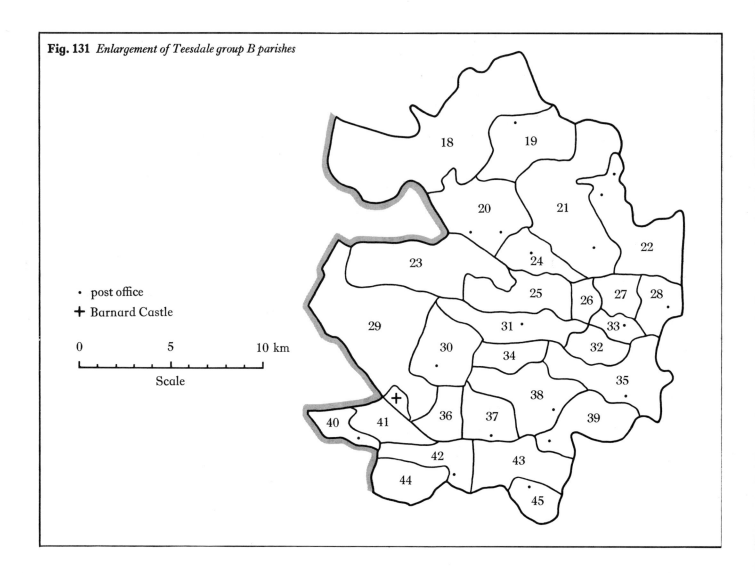

Fig. 131 *Enlargement of Teesdale group B parishes*

- post office
+ Barnard Castle

0   5   10 km

Scale

Section A

1 a A 259.35   B 536.68
   b A 10.75   B 51.02
   c A 2.73%   B 0.59%

2 a 61.67ha   b 72.50ha
   c 59.17ha   d 45.00ha

3 a A 188   B 177.50
   b A 6.5   B 18.1
   c A 4.1   B -3.35

6   A 24.85   B 7.4

7 a A 273.5   B 957
   b A 10.2   B 17.2

8 a A 186.5   B 544.04
   b A 7.66   B 47.99

9 a A 272.39   B 707.08
   b A 9.39   B 62.36
   c A 8.94   B 20.30

10 a A 77.56%   B 76.53%
   b A 105.03%   B 131.75%
   c A 87.35%   B 122.23%

27 a 68   b 95
   c 14   d 16

28 a 100   b 136
   c 95   d 27
   e 5

29 a 47.5%   b 47.5%
   c 83.85%

30 a 50%   b 68%
   c 13.5%   d 2.35%
   e 97.35%

31 a 50% ($p=0.5$)   b 95% ($p=0.95$)
   c 5% ($p=0.05$)   d approx. 3% ($p=0.03$)
   e approx. 3% ($p=0.03$)

32 a (i) 35%   (ii) 14%   (iii) 1%
   b (i) 24%   (ii) 14%   (iii) 1%

33 a (i) 35%   (ii) 3%
   b (i) 24%   (ii) 1%

Section B

1 b 040°   c 100°
   d 150°   e 212°
   f 315°

2 b 10°   c 165°
   d 165°   e 155°
   f 170°   g 155°

3 approx. 24km²

4 a approx. 31km²   b approx. 48km²

5 a Middleton-in-Teesdale = 1.21   Lartington = 10
   b Eggleston = 2.04   Holwick = 4.08
   c Newbiggin = 2   Cotherstone = 5.85

7 a gradient 1 : 8   angle 6.8°
   b gradient 1 : 32   angle 1.8°

9 $Rn = 1.41$

10 $Rn = 0.53$

11 a $Rn = 0.73$ b $Rn = 0.96$

12 a 4632   b 5055

13 Mean centre of 1965 distribution is 4334 and the 1965/1975 centre is 4629.

14 a SE = 4.07   b SE = 3.25

Section C

3 a $r_s = -0.881$ b $r_s = -0.869$
   c $r_s = 0.835$

4 a $r = -0.833$ b $r = -0.878$
   c $r = 0.826$

5 $\chi^2 = 6.93$

6 $\chi^2 = 16.3$

7 $\chi^2 = 6.27$

8 $\chi^2 = 19.98$

Index